D0193597

a Museum of Early American Tools

a MUSEUM of Early American TOOLS

by

ERIC SLOANE

BALLANTINE BOOKS • NEW YORK

Copyright © 1964 by Wilfred Funk, Inc.

All rights reserved.

Library of Congress Catalog Card Number: 64-13741

SBN 345-23571-1-200

This edition published by arrangement with Funk & Wagnalls, Inc.

First Printing: October, 1973

Printed in the United States of America

BALLANTINE BOOKS, INC.
201 East 50th Street, New York, N.Y. 10022

This sketchbook is dedicated to the unrecorded pioneer Americans who fashioned their own tools. Although mass production has made their old tools obsolete, along with Early American individualism, these ancient implements are symbols of a sincerity, an integrity, and an excellency that the unionized craftsman of today might do well to emulate.

A Special Tool
hollowing Gouge
Hay Fork
paring Adze
Draw Knife
cornering Chisel
a Hitting Mallet
Apple butter Paddle
mortising Chisel
and mortising Axe
a boring Auger
a Brace
Awl
Hewing Broad Axe
a paring Slick
a Holding Dog
a pounding Commander
hauling Sledge

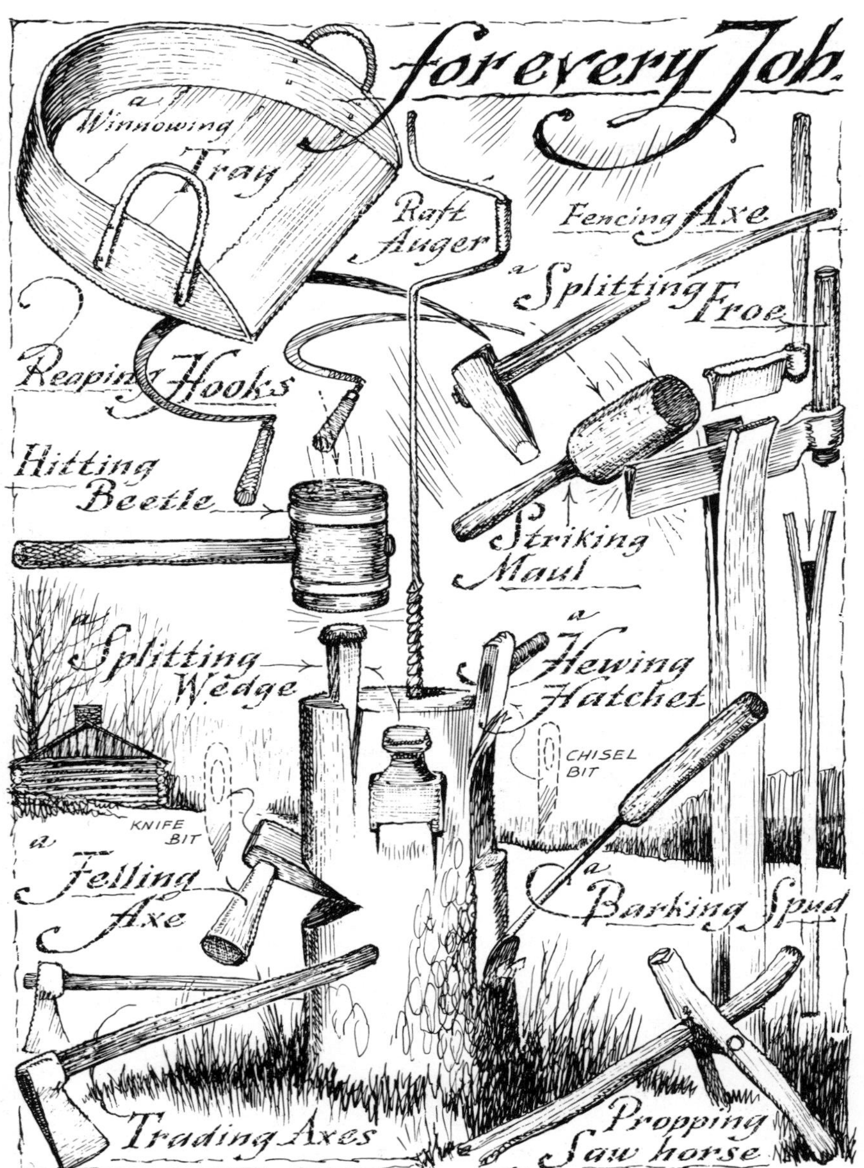
for every Job
a Winnowing Tray
Raft Auger
Fencing Axe
a Splitting Froe
Reaping Hooks
Hitting Beetle
Striking Maul
a Splitting Wedge
a Hewing Hatchet
CHISEL BIT
KNIFE BIT
a Felling Axe
a Barking Spud
Trading Axes
Propping Saw horse

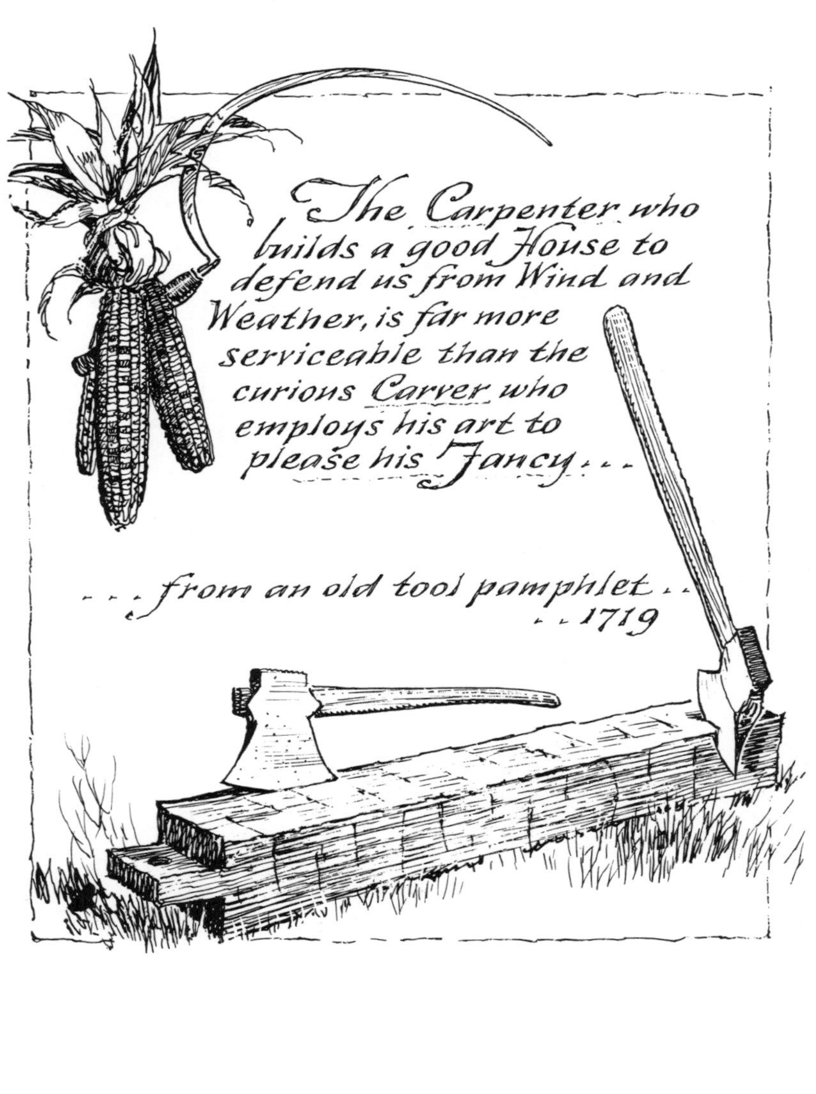
The Carpenter who builds a good House to defend us from Wind and Weather, is far more serviceable than the curious Carver who employs his art to please his Fancy . . .
. . . from an old tool pamphlet . .
. . 1719

Author's Note.

I like the sound of the word museum. Perhaps because the word root refers less to an actual collection of things than to the musing, cogitating, and reflecting that one does while beholding a collection.

Nowadays we use the word museum to identify a big, housed collection, but in the days of Early America it usually meant a simple library or some printed collection of facts. There were magazinelike books, such as "Merry's *Museum*," and there were newspaperlike publications, such as "The Farmer's *Museum*," but the fine word museum has since drifted from the world of writing. Because it is my hobby to recapture what I believe to be the good things of the past, I hope the reader will accept and enjoy my title, *A Museum of Early American Tools*.

The word magazine was first used to identify what we now might call a museum; it then meant "storehouse," or "housed collection" (powder magazine, for instance). And the first printed magazines were (like the newspapers of that day) printed on one piece of paper and folded once or perhaps twice–never in the book-form of today's magazine.

In presenting my collection of drawings as a museum, I hope that it will, like a scrapbook, induce musing and reflecting, and that it will draw the reader back into the quite different world of Early America. The rambling sequence of subjects is no accident: I would like my reader to "stroll" through this book as he would through a museum.

We might regard some of the old tools as clumsy or ugly unless we look at them in terms of the century in which they were used. Many of today's tools would have been considered ugly, clumsy, and completely undesirable by the early craftsmen. The steel and plastic handles we now have, for example, lack the spring and "feel" of seasoned wood that experts know. Shovels were made of wood not because of a lack of metal (as many assume) but because it was supposed that grain and apples were harmed by contact with metal. You might think of a wooden shovel as being short-lived, yet, although thousands of wooden shovels are to be found in antique shops and collections, almost no early metal shovels remain.

Most of today's tools have the cheapness of mass production; the old hand-made tools often had design that made them examples of fine art. Lumber cut and sold as a "two by four" was once an honest two inches by four inches; even today there are people who are shocked to learn that our lumber, because it is measured before being trimmed and planed, is sold at a quite untrue measurement. Builders who constructed rooms that were not accurately square (and why should they be?) are now regarded as slipshod and careless; yet the old buildings have stood the test much better than will many we are now building, for the joints and braces were made with much greater care than today's craftsmen consider "necessary." Floor boards were never the same width at one end as they were at the other. Quaint or poor workmanship? Not at all. The finished effect is finer than the monotony of today's narrow-width floor boards. A building pinned together with hand-whittled wooden pins? We don't have to do that sort of thing today! But if we built for lastingness and for handing down to future generations we would do so, for wooden pins work much better than nails: they hold tighter, they don't rust and rot the beams.

While I was putting this book together, my neighbor bought a good new saw and left it out overnight in the dew. Its shiny newness had given way to the orange of rust, and he telephoned me to ask for help in removing it. I took it to clean and loaned him one of my early saws to use in the meantime. The old saw was one I found in the stone wall of an ancient barn. It is still sharp and clean of rust.

And so it goes. The craftsman of yesterday might look like a poorly informed man only before we take a longer and a better look. His tools might appear pathetically poor, but his ways were honest and lasting and beautiful to an extent that is today deemed over and above requirements. How poor and dishonest and ugly and temporary are the results of so many modern workers whose constant aim is more to make the most money from their profession instead of producing the most honest and beautiful and lasting things. I feel that a good way of studying the conscience and personality of the anonymous pioneer American—so that I may emulate some of his ways—is by collecting and analyzing the tools with which he worked.

As a collector of early tools, I have also been a collector of information. Antique implements have a price tag on them, but for the information that has been priceless and gratis, I am indebted to the men at Doylestown, Shelburne, Winterthur, Cooperstown, Sturbridge, Williamsburg, and Saugus. I learned much from two excellent books, Mercer's Ancient Carpenters' Tools *and Wildung's* Woodworking Tools, *and from the Early American Industries Association's publication,* The Chronicle.

Eric Sloane

Weather Hill

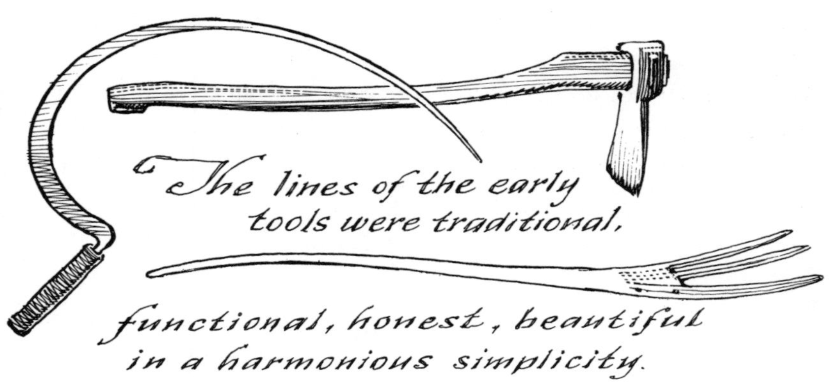

The lines of the early
tools were traditional,
functional, honest, beautiful
in a harmonious simplicity.

Contents

a Museum of Early American Tools

The Romance of Tools.

Finding an ancient tool in a stone fence or in a dark corner of some decaying barn is receiving a symbol from another world, for it gives you a particular and interesting contact with the past. Men used to build and create as much for future generations as for their own needs, so their tools have a special message for us and our time. When you hold an early implement, when you close your hand over the worn wooden handle, you know exactly how it felt to the craftsman whose hand had smoothed it to its rich patina. In that instant you are as close to that craftsman as you can be—even closer than if you live in the house that he built or sit in the chair that he made. In that moment you are near to another being in another life, and you are that much richer.

Why an ancient tool should be closer to the early craftsman than a modern tool is to a modern workman is not readily understood by most people. Even the ardent collector is sometimes unaware of the reason an ancient tool meant so much to its user. But reason there is. Henry Ward Beecher said it nicely when he explained that "a tool is but the extension of a man's hand." Whereas today's implements are designed with the idea of "getting a job done quickly," there was an added quality to the early implements and an added quality to early workmanship too. For, like the nails on a beast's paws, the old tools were so much an extension of a man's hand or an added appendage to his arm, that the resulting workmanship seemed to flow directly from the body of the maker and to carry something of himself into the work. True, by looking at an old house or an old piece of furniture, you can imagine the maker much more clearly than you can by beholding anything made today.

The early implement was also a piece of art, as much as the work it

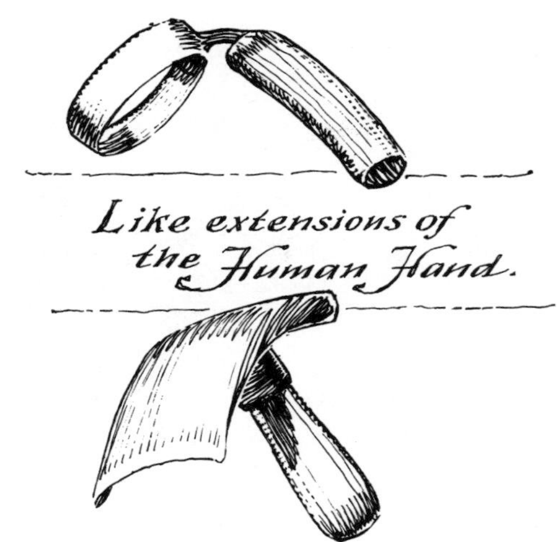
Like extensions of
the Human Hand.

fashioned, for the worker designed his tools too. In Early America the ironworkers forged only the cutting blade; they gave no thought to the design of the wooden handle and the rest of the finished tool. Plane blades and even knife-blades were hand-forged and sold like axe heads, and the craftsman was left to make his own wooden "hand" to hold the "fingernail," or cutting part. A small hand needed a small handle and a big hand needed a big handle; the man who used an apprentice had notches in his big plane that enabled the apprentice to help push it along with a stick.

A man whose architectural creations followed the Greek or Roman tradition would find it natural to include Greek or Roman artistic touches in the ornamentation of his implements. Decoration on the early tool, however, sprang from the pride of the maker rather than from any custom.

The feeling that certain tools had souls of their own was not unusual; an axe might be marked "Tom" or "Jack" simply because the owner felt it was a companion worthy of a pet name. All this sounds strangely superstitious. Yet today motor trucks are often named "Sally" or "Babe"; boats almost always have names; even large machine tools, such as presses or bulldozers, are graced with pet names.

Sacred initials on one side, the date on the other.

The religious man probably felt that sacred initials or Biblical quotations might have their effect upon the work done by that tool. Perhaps mindful that the carpenter Jesus once worked with such tools, some of the early woodworking implements have crosses carved upon them.

One of the finer pieces in a recent showing of modern art was a piece of steel that curved like a bird's wing. It was set into a square block of wood and its title in the catalogue was "Number 1760." The artist had an even more honest sense of beauty than a sense of humor, for if you looked closely and with an informed eye, you could recognize the piece as the head of an Early American "goose wing" broad axe. In the back of the blade, the year 1760 had been marked, which, of course, explained the title. To many it was, at first, the most beautiful piece of art there,

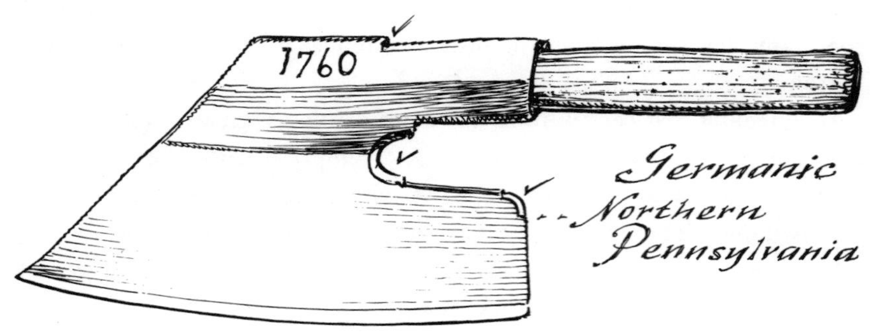

but when they learned that it was only an old axe head, they felt as if they had been hoaxed. How, after all, could an axe head be considered a work of art!

The Civil War period marked a turning point in tool design, as it did for so much Americana. Before that time, the word tool meant an implement that could make one thing at a time; mass-production tools then entered the scene, and the word tool, which had meant only "hand tool," took on many added meanings. Finally the word tool came to mean any item having to do with the production of an item; it could be the machine and also the building that housed the machine. Even the salesmen, the advertising gadgets, and the business offices are "tools of the trade."

Generally speaking, hand tools made after the Civil War period lacked the simple beauty of those of the ante-bellum period. Things were made to sell quickly, things were made in large quantities so that they could be catalogued identically, and hand-made implements began to disappear. Wooden handles became "fancier," more curved and ornamental, but the severe beauty of folk art and primitive usage was lost. Saw handles became "trickier"; they were designed to appeal to the eye instead of to fit the hand. Axe handles, which had always been almost straight, as a good club should be, took on curves such as the "fawn foot" and the "scroll knob." By 1885, handles on axes and adzes had become almost too curved, but by the 1900's they settled down to a sensible and standard design, such as that of those you can buy now at the hardware store.

Before the Civil War, most axe handles (like the handles of all tools) were made by the man who would use the axe. A pattern was cut from a piece of flat wood and saved as the model from which future handles would be fashioned. Axe patterns (which you can still find in old barns) were so subtly curved and proportioned that they were as distinctive as a man's signature; you could take one look and say "This tool belongs to Jones" or "That tool belongs to Smith." Very often an axe-handle pattern was handed down from generation to generation, and it was considered counterfeit for another family to copy it.

While we are on the subject of the handles of old tools, I would like to point out that the collector should understand something of the philosophy about the connection between the workman's hand and that part of a hand tool that he touches. Most modern workmen will scoff at the idea, but any fine craftsman will tell you that the right wooden handle (let us say, on a hammer) helps you along with your work. A metal or plastic handle or even an incorrect wooden handle can feel "dead" and not "spring back" against pressure, thus causing blisters and slowing your work. The proper handle's "feel" or "heft" is the unexplainable quality that a fine violin has to the musician. *The Oxford History of Technology* quotes Christian Barman's comments on an exhibition of early hand tools: "Everybody who appreciates the qualities of materials loves wood, and here was wood formed into a special kind of tactile sculpture made to be felt with the hand. I remembered that old craftsmen, when they buy a new set of modern chisels, throw away the handles and carefully fit their own. These handles, polished bright by a lifetime of use, became part of their owners' lives."

Always in the fine art of working with wood, the old-time craftsman's laboratory was in his head and his hands and his heart. He called it "knack"; some now believe it was a "sixth sense" or an extrasensory power. Elusive as this "knack" may be, it is the most important part of those small differences that distinguish the master craftsman from the good workman.

When we consider tools, we are dealing with human benefactors of the most primary sort. Tools increase and vary human power; they economize human time, and they convert raw substances into valuable and useful products. So when we muse on historic tools as symbols, we are always analyzing the romance of human progress.

Although Early American tools were traditional in design to such an extent that one can usually tell the nationality of the maker, there are almost always subtle differences and decorative touches in design that equally identify the region of American countryside from which the tool came. A collector can easily tell a piece coming from Pennsylvania from one originating in Connecticut. This distinctiveness was often intentional; the Early American's urge for identification was born of pride both in himself and in his time. An extraordinary awareness of life and time permeated our early days; when something was made and the maker was satisfied, it wasn't complete until his mark and the date were added.

Nowadays things are almost obsolete before they leave the drawing board. How lucky we are that so many of the old tools and the things that were made with them were dated and touched with the craftsman's art.

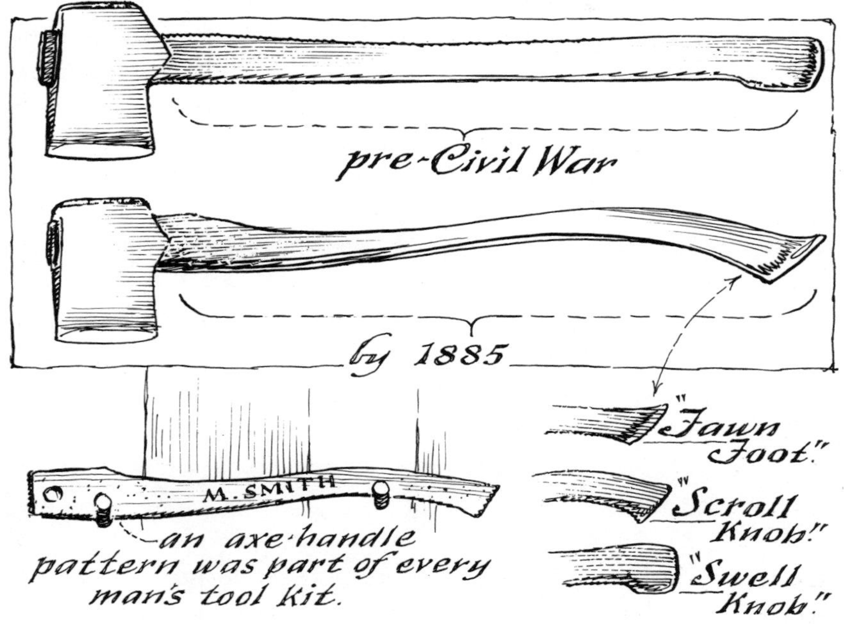

Crude Shops,
Magnificent
Results.

After the Civil War, factory-made things became popular and the tool house was limited to such minor work as farm repairs. The Dominy Shop (shown below) was used by Nathaniel Dominy IV (1737–1812) and his son Nathaniel V (1770–1852). This entire shop, including manuscript accounts covering the period from 1762 until 1829, has been kept intact at the Henry Francis du Pont Winterthur Museum in Delaware. The visitor's first reaction is usually "What a primitive shop!" Yet the magnificent table standing in the center of the room was made in it.

Courtesy, Henry Francis du Pont Winterthur Museum

Tool House in Berks County Pennsylvania
an old-time Carpenter-bench
PLANK TO BE SAWED AT X IS HELD AND LIFTED BY
Side Rest
X
BENCH HOOK
A
HOLES FOR BENCH HOOKS
Horizontal Bench vise
HOLES FOR A
Hold-fast
FOR CLAMPING DOWN BOARDS.
A
Vertical vise
Bench Clamp
B
Block Knife
Block Hook
PIECE OF WOOD HELD BY STOP A B IN A
Box Vise

An Ax is an Axe!

No matter how you spell it (both ways are correct), it is natural to start off a sketchbook of Early American implements with this tool. America was a new world of unending wood where a man armed with only a felling axe could enter the forest and survive. With his axe he could clear the land of trees, cut fuel, build a bridge, a house, and furniture. With his axe he could fashion snares for game and, in a pinch, use it to protect himself against marauding Indians or wild beasts. No wonder the first settlers carried axes in their belts and treated them with a respect like that of a soldier toward his sword or side arms.

As was true of all first American artifacts, our earliest axes were like those from abroad. They had well-curved, gracefully fashioned blades, and they lacked the bulky polls such as those that identify the pure American design. The heavy poll appears to be for hammering (indeed it could have been used for such), yet it was devised to serve as a weight to give more momentum to chopping. Few early polless axes have survived except those traded with the Indians (trade axes).

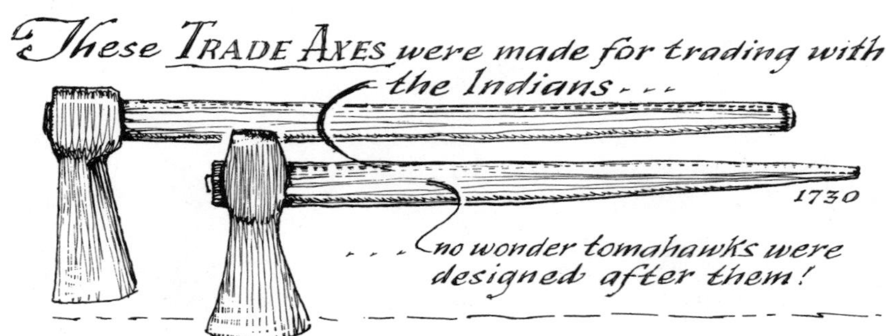

These TRADE AXES were made for trading with the Indians . . .
1730
. . . no wonder tomahawks were designed after them!

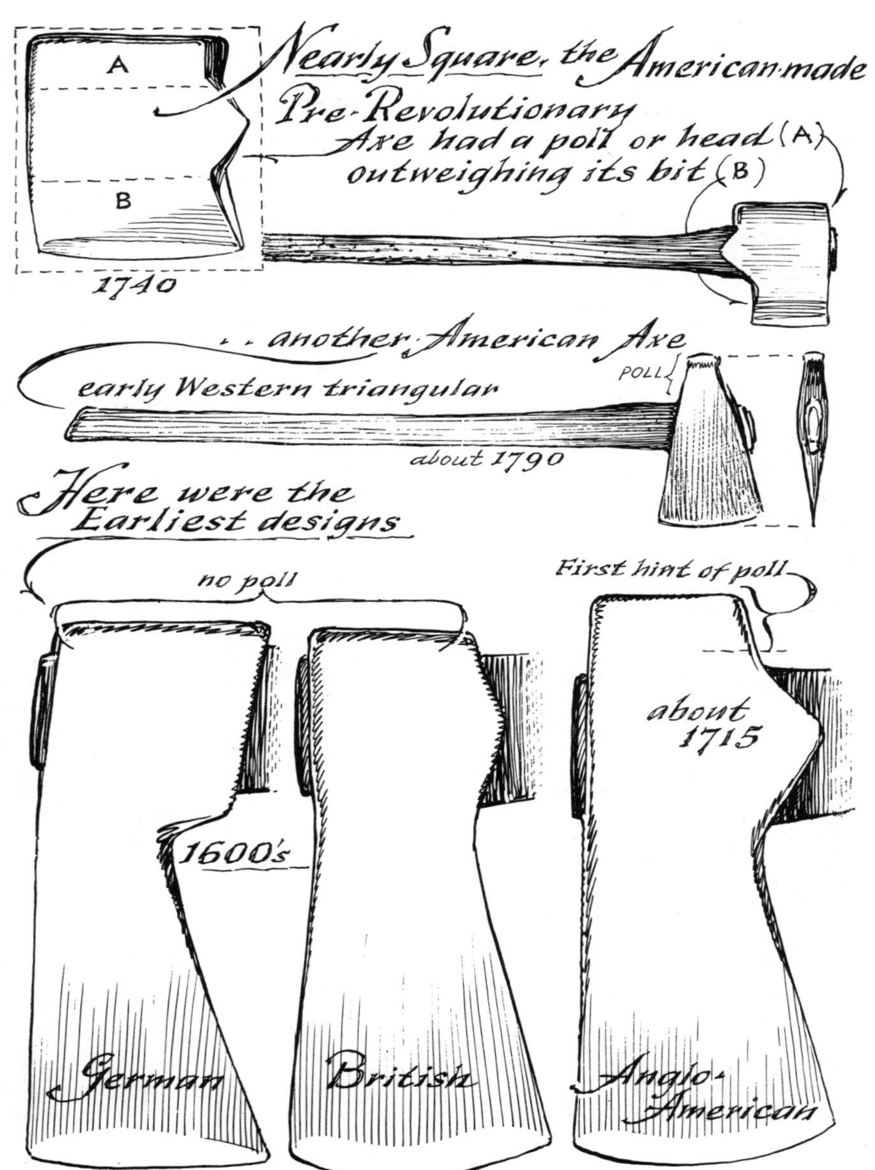
Nearly Square, the American-made
Pre-Revolutionary
Axe had a poll or head (A)
outweighing its bit (B)
A
B
1740
. . another American Axe
early Western triangular
POLL
about 1790
Here were the
Earliest designs
no poll
First hint of poll
1600's
about
1715
German
British
Anglo-
American

A World of Axes

America's wealth of wood and her pride in carpenter craftsmanship resulted in an amazing array of specialty tools. Early catalogues listed more than fifty patterns of axe heads alone, all doing the same jobs yet differing in design. Farmers and blacksmiths fashioned their own axes for framing and for mortising the beams of barns (shown below) or for felling trees (shown opposite).

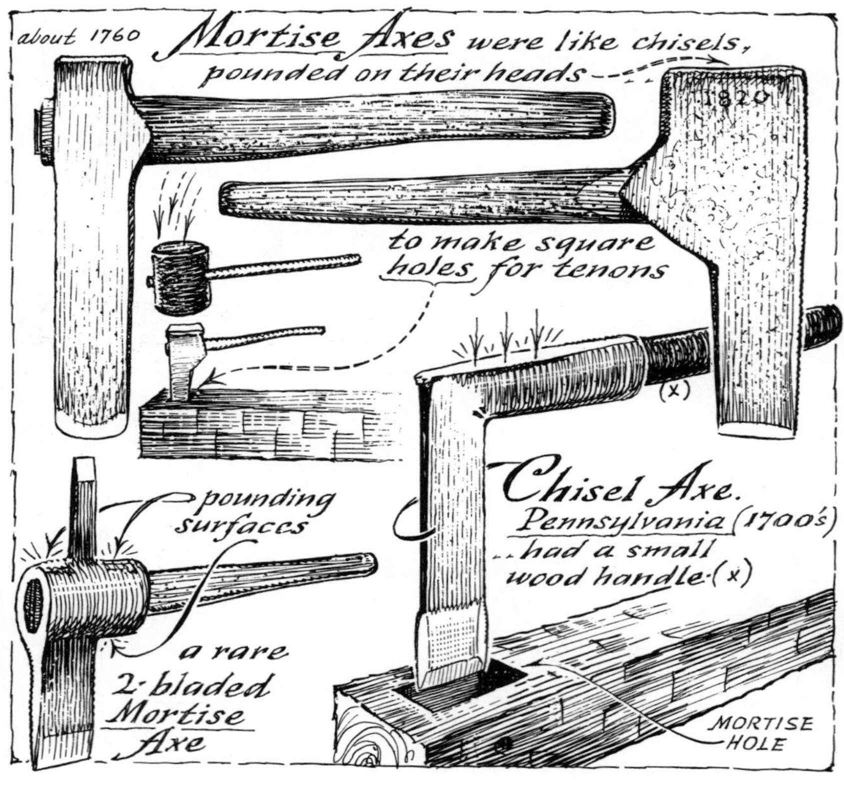

about 1760
Mortise Axes were like chisels, pounded on their heads
1820
to make square holes for tenons
(x)
pounding surfaces
a rare 2-bladed Mortise Axe
Chisel Axe.
Pennsylvania (1700's)
..had a small wood handle·(x)
MORTISE HOLE

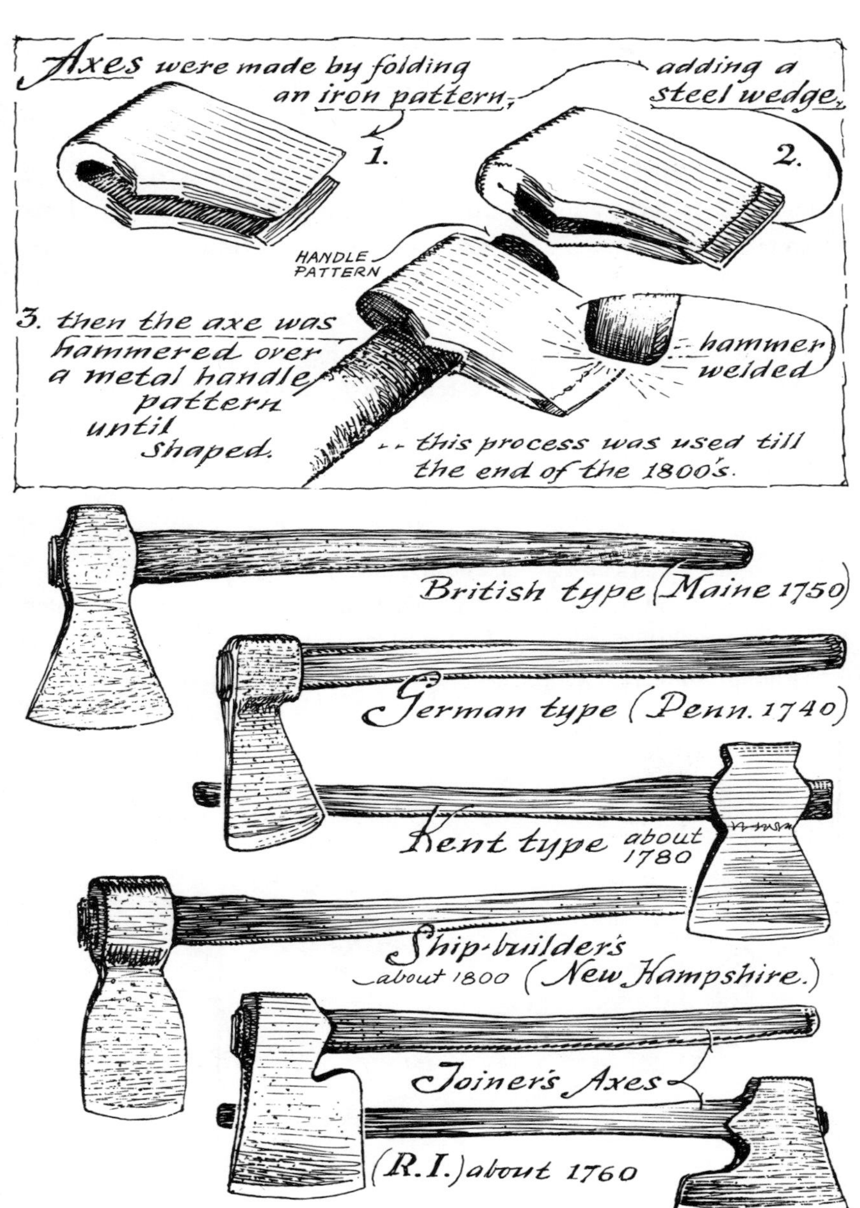
Axes were made by folding
an iron pattern,
adding a
steel wedge,
1.
2.
HANDLE PATTERN
3. then the axe was
hammered over
a metal handle
pattern
until
shaped.
hammer
welded
.. this process was used till
the end of the 1800's.
British type (Maine 1750)
German type (Penn. 1740)
Kent type about
1780
Ship-builder's
about 1800 (New Hampshire.)
Joiner's Axes
(R.I.) about 1760

The Broad Axe.

A most essential Early American tool was the chisel-edged broad axe. Thousands of them are still around, but people seeing this broad axe often take it for a very big and clumsy felling axe. Because few museums bother either to include the tool or to explain its use, few people really know how it was used. Actually, it was a kind of plane or striking chisel that early Americans used for hewing round logs into square beams.

More than twice the size of a felling axe, this tool had a short bent handle protruding outward from the side of the axe head with the bevel (basil or chisel-slant) on that same side. Two hands were used; the process was called "squaring" or "hewing."

The American-style broad axe had a fair-sized squarish head, or poll (as the other American-style axes did); European types had none.

Although hand-hewn timbers in old buildings are commonly called "adzed beams," they were usually broad-axed.

Although some odd people hack up beams "to make them appear hand done," the most expert broad-axe man cut the fewest axe marks, and those that were left were spaced nicely—never haphazardly.

Never haphazard!

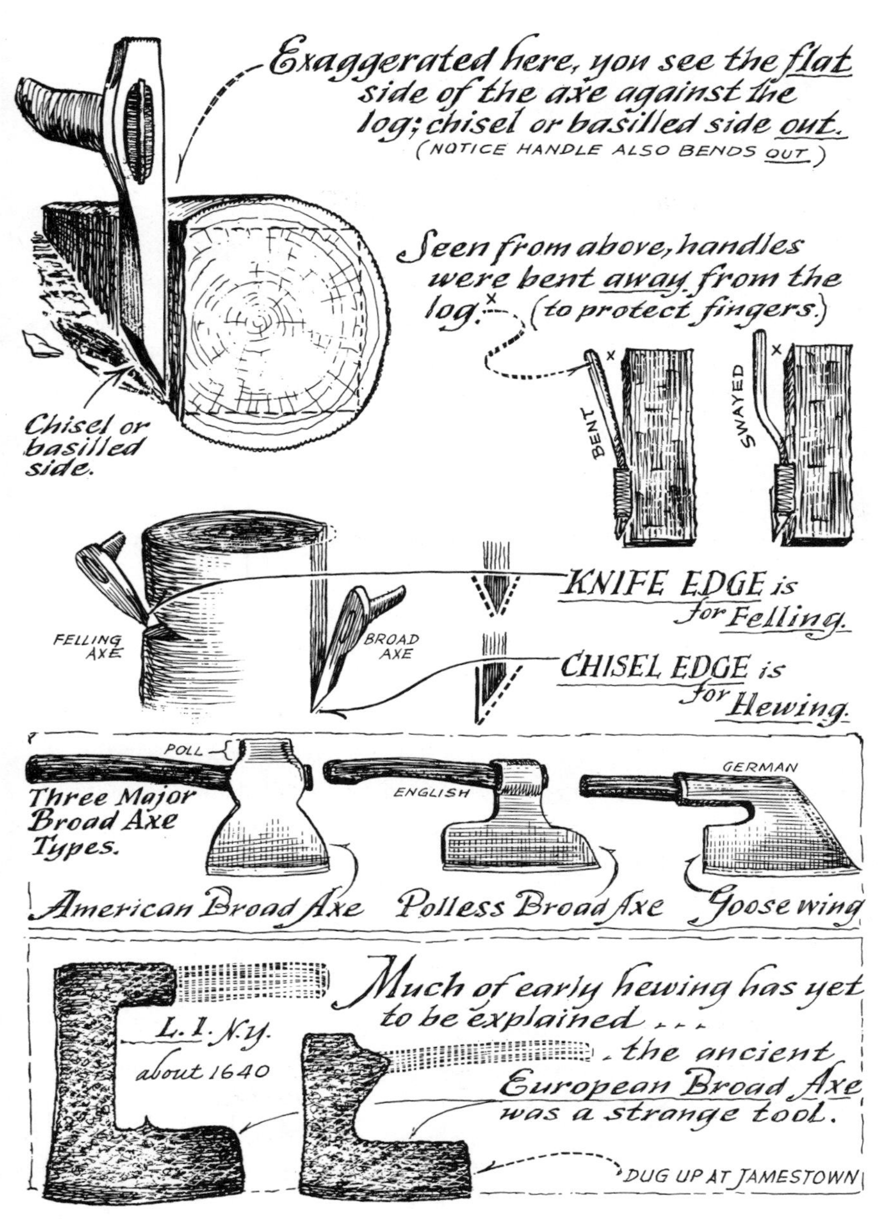
Exaggerated here, you see the flat side of the axe against the log; chisel or basilled side out.
(NOTICE HANDLE ALSO BENDS OUT)
Chisel or basilled side.
Seen from above, handles were bent away from the log.x (to protect fingers.)
x
BENT
x
SWAYED
FELLING AXE
BROAD AXE
KNIFE EDGE is for Felling.
CHISEL EDGE is for Hewing.
POLL
Three Major Broad Axe Types.
ENGLISH
GERMAN
American Broad Axe
Polless Broad Axe
Goose wing
Much of early hewing has yet to be explained . . .
L. I. N.Y.
about 1640
. the ancient European Broad Axe was a strange tool.
DUG UP AT JAMESTOWN

How the Broad Axe was Used

Any old-timer is willing to tell you how to use a broad axe, but each one is bound to describe a different method. Trying to ferret out the truth I asked everyone who visited my collection—if the visitor claimed he knew the art—to demonstrate broad-axing. Some "used to stand upon the log, hewing as they walked along it." "But you wouldn't be able to reach the log with so short a handle! You'd chop your toes off!" was my reply. But they insisted, and offered to demonstrate. The doctor managed to sew one toe back on very nicely.

Actually, a walk-along-the-log method was used, but with a special broad axe unlike the ancient ones with bent handles. (This is shown on the following page.) As for the ancient chisel-edged broad axe, you walked *alongside* the log, working as you went. One man would swing horizontally (with the grain); another would hit straight downward; another would strike at an angle. As for me, I contend there was no generally accepted procedure. Mercer (in *Ancient Carpenters' Tools*) says that the broad axe was usually "held with both hands, right hand foremost. The leg face was set against the workman's left side and he hewed with both hands, not longways with the grain but diagonally *downward* across it."

"DOGS" were used to fasten logs to be worked upon.
two types

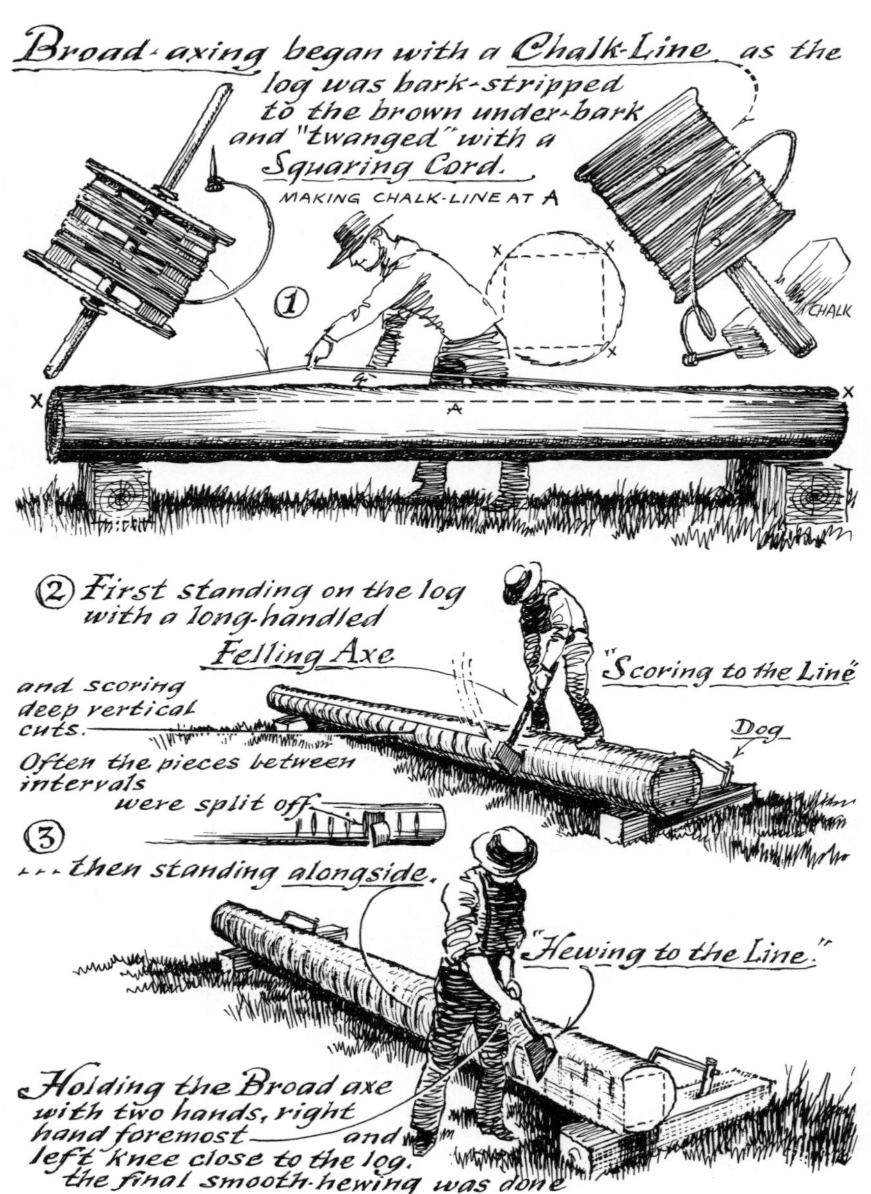
Broad-axing began with a Chalk-Line as the
log was bark-stripped
to the brown under-bark
and "twanged" with a
Squaring Cord.
MAKING CHALK-LINE AT A
①
CHALK
A
② First standing on the log
with a long-handled
Felling Axe
and scoring
deep vertical
cuts.
"Scoring to the Line"
Dog
Often the pieces between
intervals
were split off
③
... then standing alongside.
"Hewing to the Line."
Holding the Broad axe
with two hands, right
hand foremost
and
left knee close to the log.
the final smooth-hewing was done

A Giant and a Midget.

The straight-handled broad axe—a knife-edged axe beveled on both sides—was usually used to hew railroad ties. Logging railroads that make their ties out of softwood hew just two sides of the log. A tree was felled at a slight angle (held at one end by its own branches), and the hewer walked first up and then down, flattening the sides as he went. The same axe was used both for scoring and hewing! This process seems difficult but it was fast.

Because this axe has a straight handle, it is often mistaken for some re-handled ancient broad axe, ground on two sides to convert it into a felling axe. The only clue to its true use is that its ponderous head is much too heavy to swing sideways as an axe must be swung in felling.

The smallest version of the hewing axe is the carpenter's hewing hatchet (below). It sometimes looks like a toy model of the big one. Never used to split wood or to drive nails, these hatchets were used for shaping.

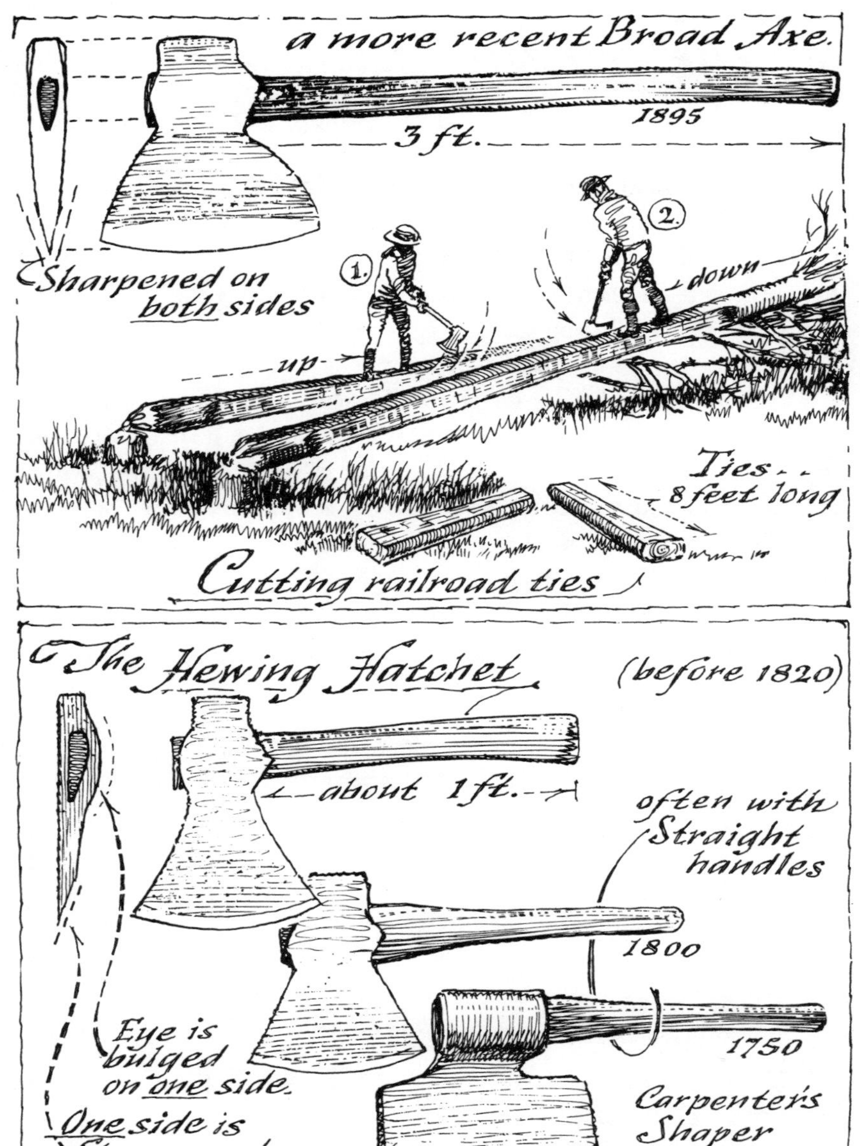
a more recent Broad Axe.
1895
3 ft.
Sharpened on both sides
1.
2.
up
down
Ties . . 8 feet long
Cutting railroad ties
The Hewing Hatchet
(before 1820)
about 1 ft.
often with Straight handles
1800
1750
Eye is bulged on one side.
One side is Sharpened.
Carpenter's Shaper

The Hatchet.

Today's household hatchet began as the "shingling hatchet." This had a flared shape with slightly rounded nail-hammering head and a nail-pulling notch in the bit. Because the first New World roofs were thatched, shingling hatchets were unknown to the early settler. Shingling hatchets so often fell from roofs being worked on that roofers frequently had them strung for hanging at the wrist.

The "lathing hatchet" is recognized by its flat outside contour, made so nails could be struck near a ceiling without hitting it. If the axe head flared, the flare was on the inside of the bit. It soon became the favorite carpenter's tool to replace the awkward cooper's hatchet. (See opposite. The cooper rounding off a barrel head is using a cooper's hatchet; notice how it was held close to its head rather than by the end of its handle.)

The 1790 American axe-hatchet (shown below) was a miniature model of the square-headed American axe with the poll that outweighed the bit.

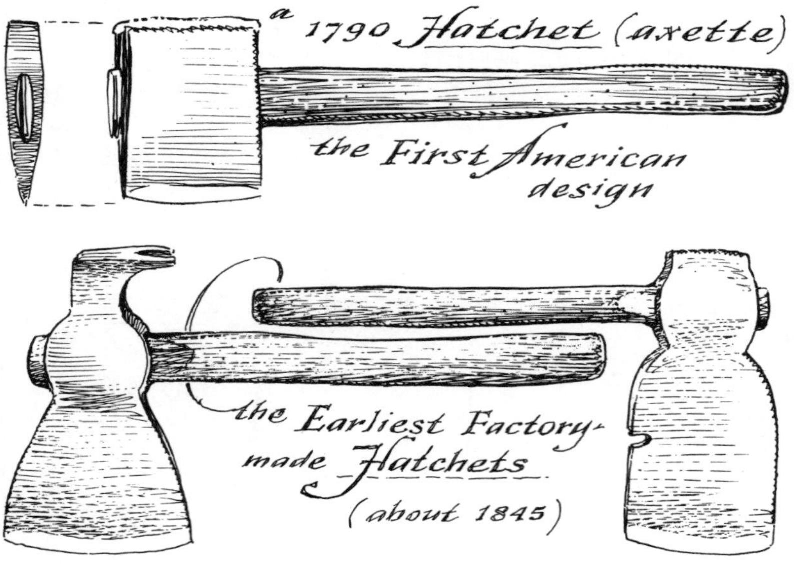

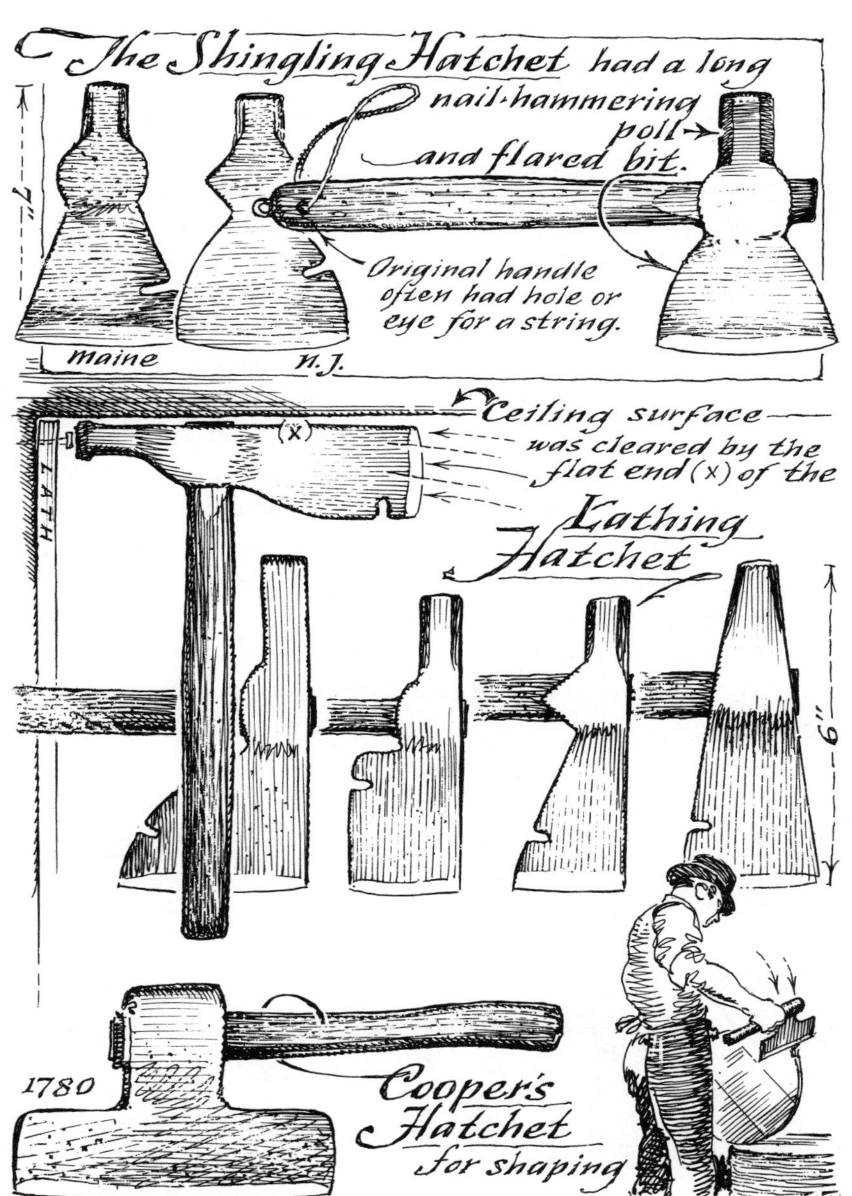
The Shingling Hatchet had a long nail-hammering poll and flared bit.
7"
maine
N.J.
Original handle often had hole or eye for a string.
Ceiling surface was cleared by the flat end (x) of the
(x)
LATH
Lathing Hatchet
6"
1780
Cooper's Hatchet for shaping

Hammers

The claw hammer hasn't changed much since about 75 A.D. Aside from its aesthetic qualities, the Roman example shown below has a most efficient design (which might do well to show up any day now).

The use of nails in the 1600's and the 1700's was more efficient then than now. The early square-cut nails, for instance, had greater holding power than our round nails; furthermore, they retarded splitting of the wood. The practice of "clinching" (bending over the protruding point) is now regarded as poor workmanship, but its efficiency is obvious. Early batten doors with wrought nails on the outside and bent points on the inside are cemented together so well that it is next to impossible to pry them apart.

Perhaps the rarity of ancient iron hammers in America is due to the once widespread practice of using wooden mallets to drive in wooden nails (tree-nails or trunnels), even wooden nails of a tiny toothpick size. Wooden mallets were also used as striking chisels; iron hammers, *only* for metal nails.

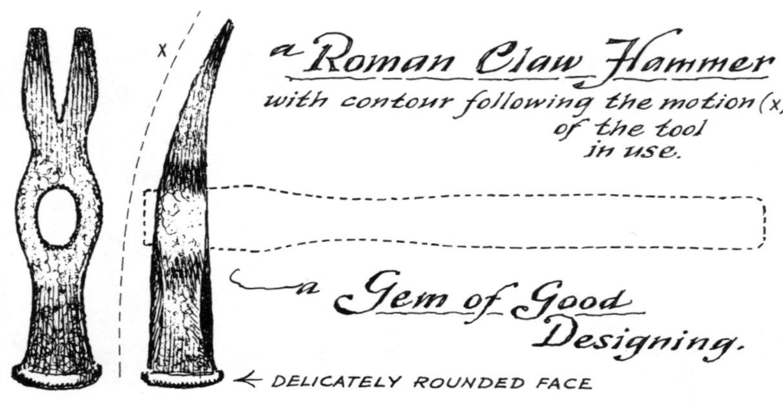

x
a Roman Claw Hammer
with contour following the motion (x) of the tool in use.
a Gem of Good Designing.
DELICATELY ROUNDED FACE

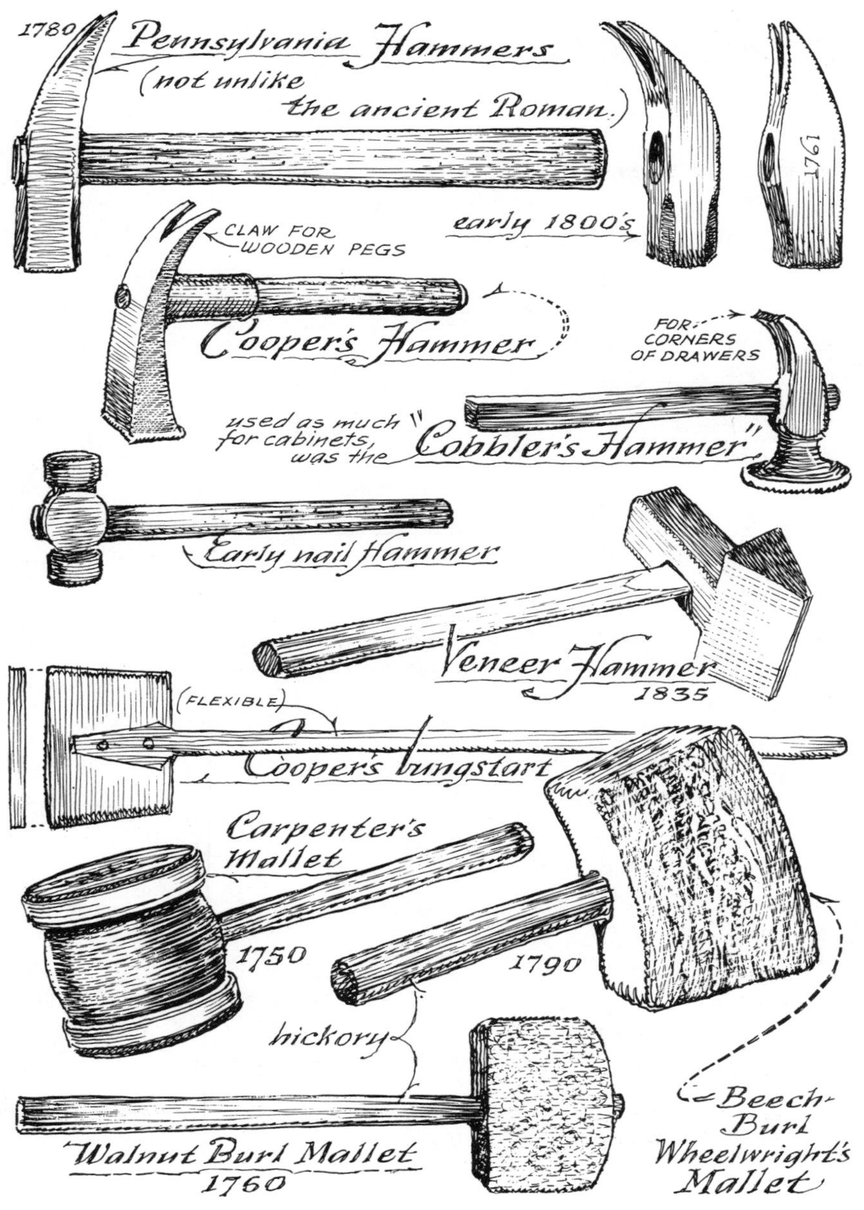
1780
Pennsylvania Hammers
(not unlike the ancient Roman.)
early 1800's
CLAW FOR WOODEN PEGS
Cooper's Hammer
FOR CORNERS OF DRAWERS
used as much for cabinets, was the "Cobbler's Hammer"
Early nail Hammer
Veneer Hammer
1835
(FLEXIBLE)
Cooper's bungstart
Carpenter's Mallet
1750
1790
hickory
Walnut Burl Mallet
1760
Beech-Burl Wheelwright's Mallet

The Axe and the Log House.

Before we leave the subject of axes, the reader will be interested in seeing just what was expected of the axe. Here are some standard log-house notches often made with only the axe.

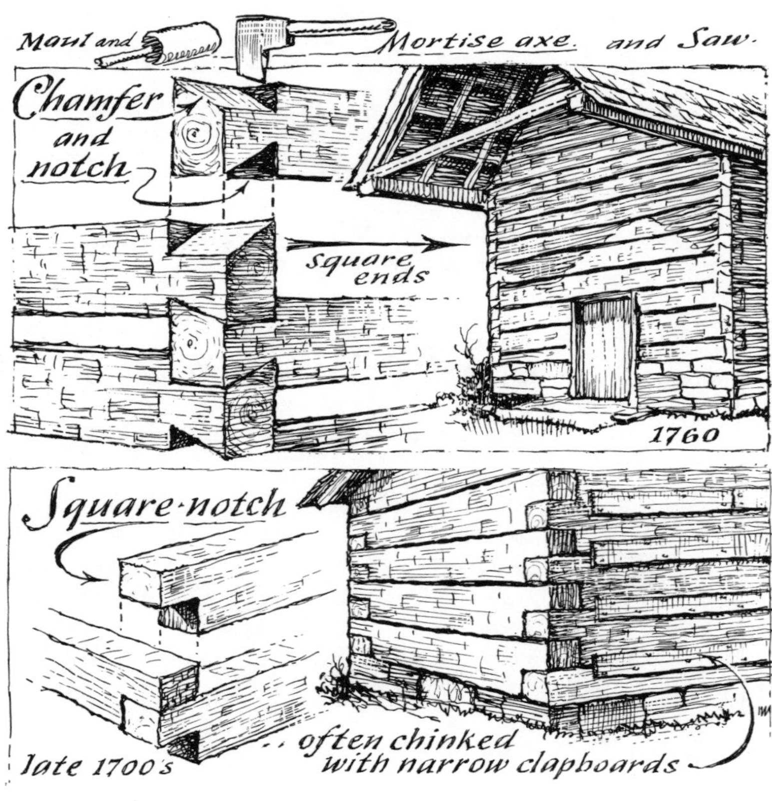

Saddle-notch
1. Axe cut
2. Gutter Adze to round out

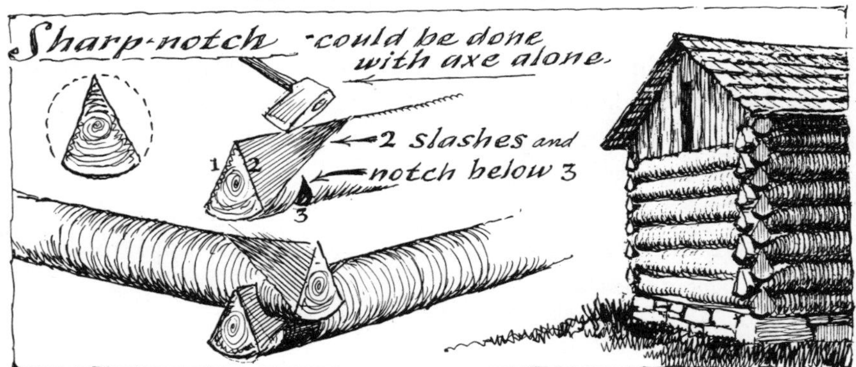
Sharp-notch -could be done with axe alone.
2 slashes and notch below 3
1
2
3

Dovetail-notch came from Sweden (c.1640)
Lip adze and axe.
upper notch slants out to drain rain.

The Adze

The idea of a sharp tool with its blade at a right angle to the handle is most ancient. The Early American version was swung in the curvature of the blade, with the arm and tool forming the radius.

Because of its flaring square end, the adze head had to be removable (as the bevel to be sharpened was on the inside and inaccessible to a grindstone). Some of the earliest adzes, however, had nonremovable heads, which had to be sharpened with a whetstone.

The shipwright's adze had a long peg-poll for driving down broken nails (and to prevent the blade from being nicked).

As shown below, the right-angle cuts on old beams are make-ready scorings for broad-axe work, not so-called "adze marks." Only on special "parlor beams" (these were made to be exposed) was the adze introduced; then the surface effect was from a delicate ripple to almost complete smoothness.

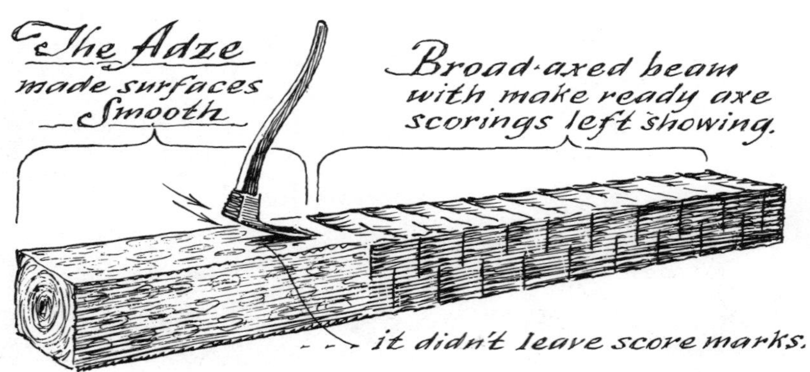
The Adze
made surfaces
Smooth
Broad-axed beam
with make ready axe
scorings left showing.
it didn't leave score marks.

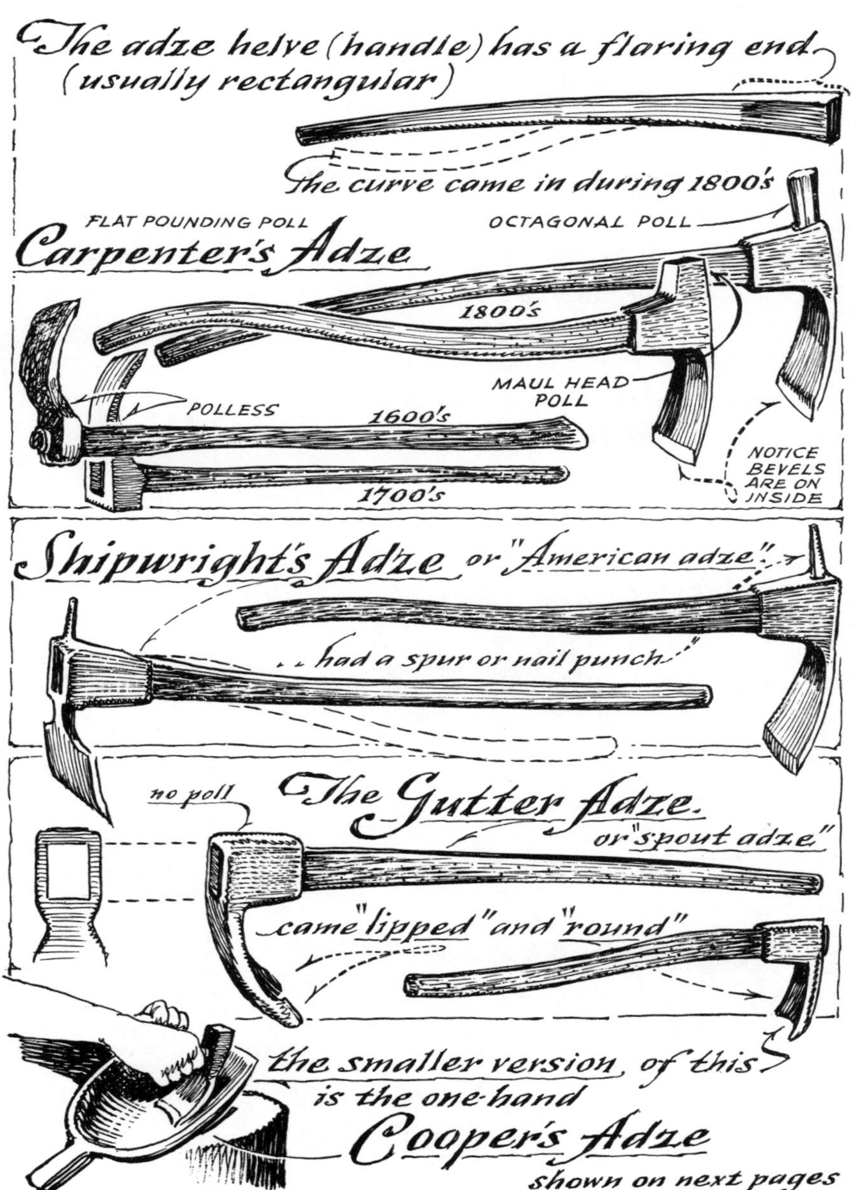
The adze helve (handle) has a flaring end (usually rectangular)
The curve came in during 1800's
FLAT POUNDING POLL
OCTAGONAL POLL
Carpenter's Adze
1800's
MAUL HEAD POLL
POLLESS
1600's
1700's
NOTICE BEVELS ARE ON INSIDE
Shipwright's Adze or "American adze"
. . had a spur or nail punch
no poll
The Gutter Adze.
or "spout adze"
came "lipped" and "round"
the smaller version of this is the one-hand
Cooper's Adze
shown on next pages

Canoes and Bowls

The word canoe (canow and canoo in the 1600's) described a hollowed-out log. Until the Indians saw the English hand adze, they used fire to burn out the hollow portion and flint knives and shells to scrape out the burned wood. Then they devised their own adze, using flint instead of metal for the blade. The scoop, or scorp, became refined as the years went by, and, finally, it became a finishing tool.

Maple and ash burls (wartlike bumps on tree trunks) were first burned and then scorped out, making the toughest and most durable of all bowls.

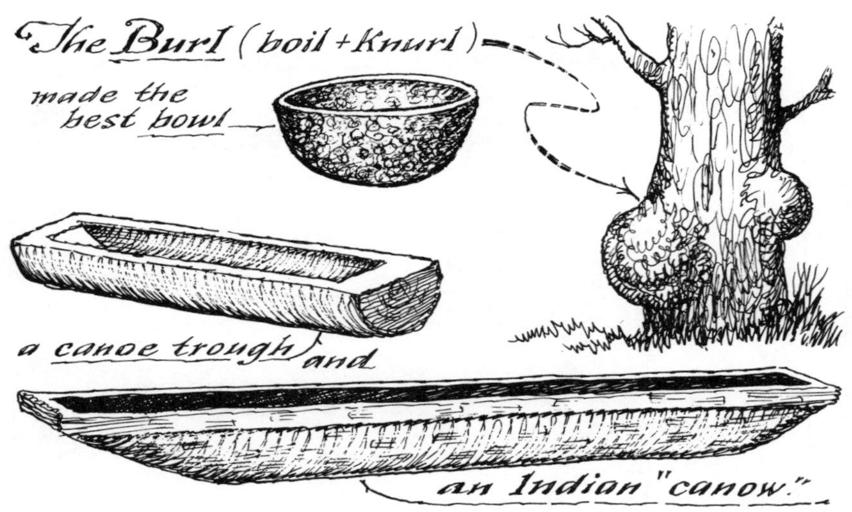
The Burl (boil + Knurl)
made the best bowl
a canoe trough and
an Indian "canow."

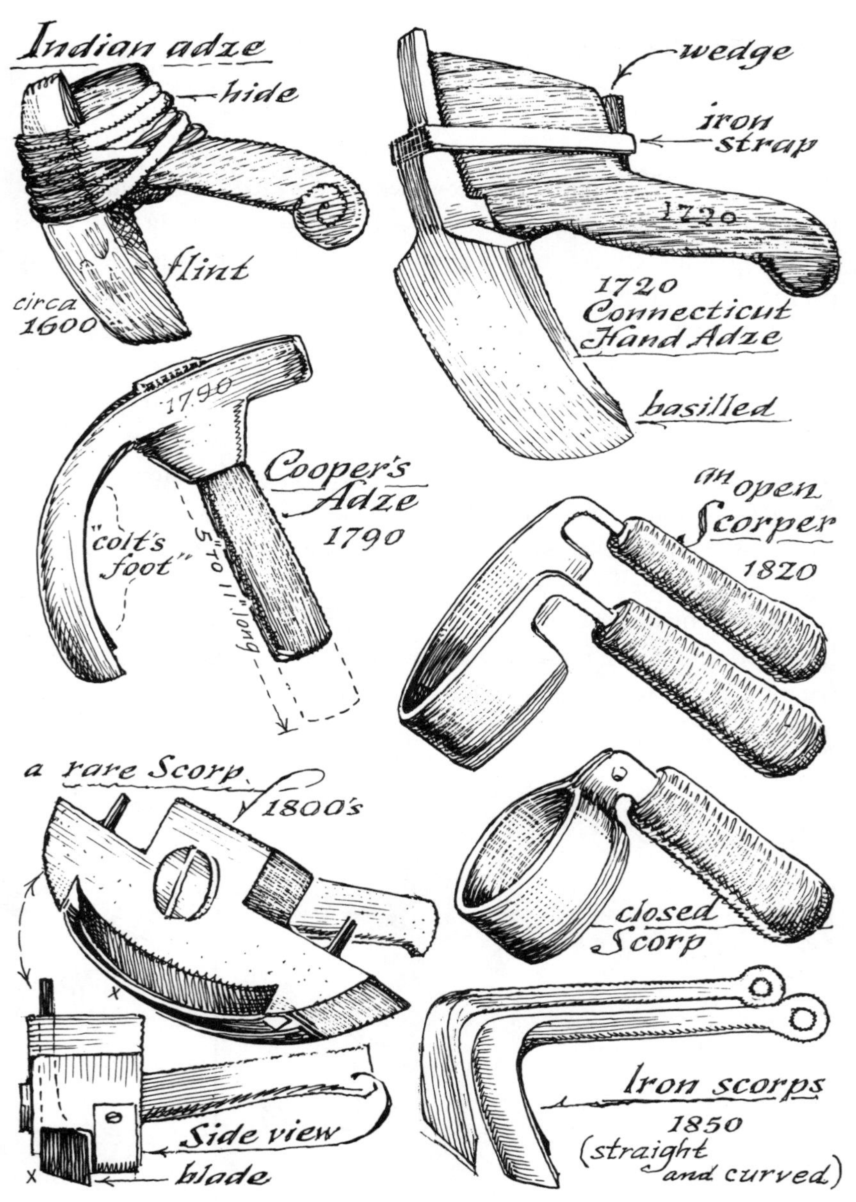
Indian adze
hide
flint
circa 1600
wedge
iron strap
1720
1720 Connecticut Hand Adze
basilled
1790
Cooper's Adze 1790
"colt's foot"
5" to 11" long
an open Scorper 1820
a rare Scorp 1800's
closed Scorp
Side view
blade
Iron scorps
1850 (straight and curved)

Wedges and Froes

A good woodsman would never consider using his axe as a hammer to hit the head of a wedge. That would not only widen the eye but also would finally split the cheeks, finishing off the axe head forever. Yet many paintings of Lincoln show him splitting rails with an axe. Rails were split with wedges. Iron wedges (or wooden gluts) were driven into the wood with a heavy maul or beetle (as shown below).

To split shingles, laths, staves, and clapboards, a knife-type wedge called a froe or frow (shown on the opposite page) was struck with a short maul known as a froe-club. In England the froe is known also as a fromard or rending-axe. The clapboard-maker struck away from himself and twisted the froe handle to split the board with the grain, while striking away with the froe-club (see drawing).

The froe became obsolete about a century ago, when it became customary to saw-cut shingles and laths. Till then, "riving" shingles was a favorite rainy-day woodshed job, and every household had several froes on hand.

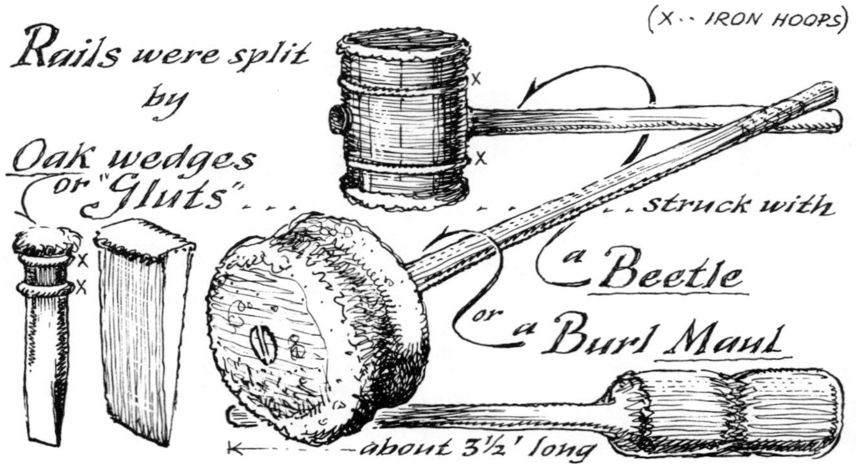
(X.. IRON HOOPS)
Rails were split by Oak wedges or "Gluts"
X
X
X
X
struck with a Beetle or a Burl Maul
about 3½' long

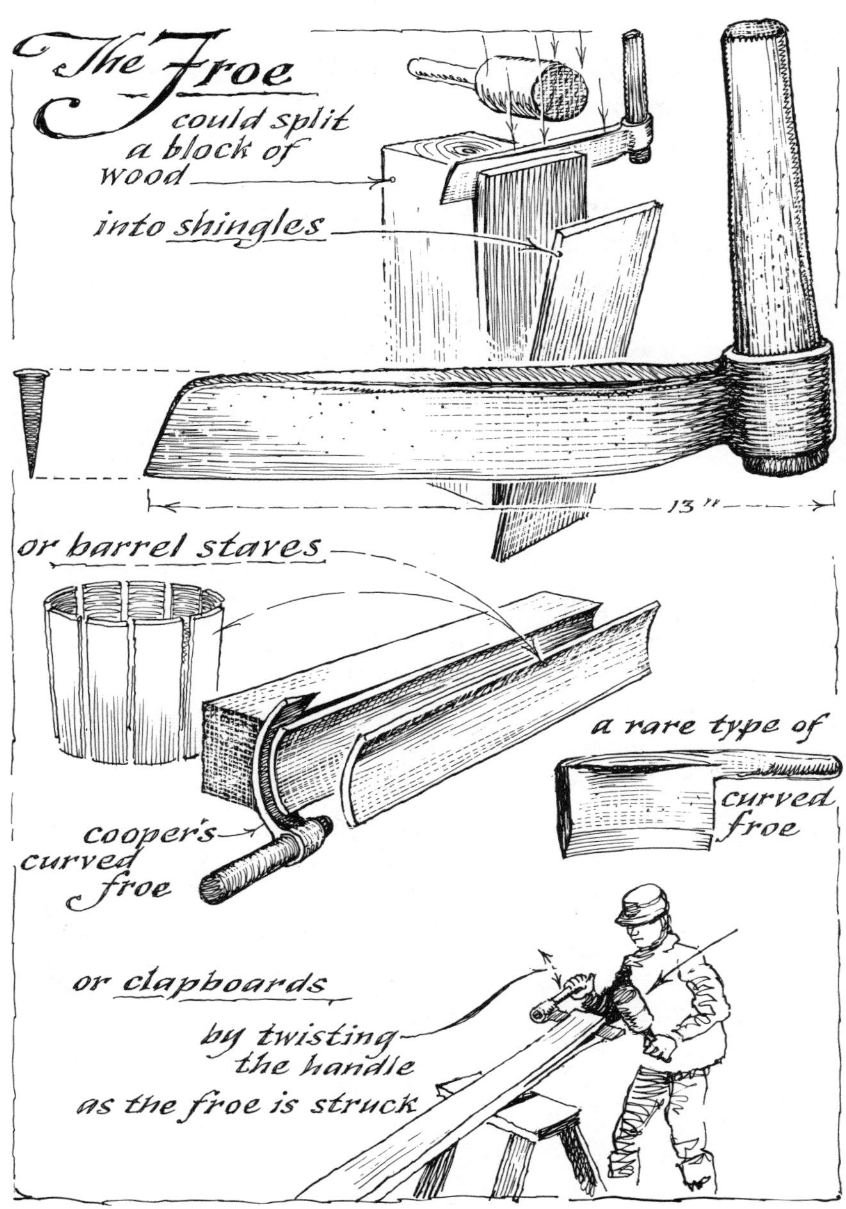
The Froe
could split
a block of
wood
into shingles
13"
or barrel staves
a rare type of
curved
froe
cooper's
curved
froe
or clapboards
by twisting
the handle
as the froe is struck

The Fine Art of Splitting.

The uses of the froe were many. Very old men, too feeble to swing an axe, were given the chore of splitting kindling from logs. Half-round barrel hoops were also split with the froe. Willow poles were split in half for making gates and hurdles. The early hurdle was not like our horse hurdle; it was a section of fence that could be lashed to other similar sections to make a portable animal enclosure.

Lathing was split with the froe from fresh oak, in both single strips and "flats." Lath flats were split first on one side, then the other, making a sort of accordion piece that could be unfolded.

The saw was almost never used for cutting with the grain or lengthwise: splitting a length of wood was so much easier. A craftsman could split inch-square lengths from a large piece of wood in a fraction of the time that it would take him to saw them.

Because of the many uses of the froe, there is hardly an old barn left that doesn't have a number of these tools tucked away somewhere in it. Less ubiquitous, however, are their battered mates, the froe-clubs.

No need for a saw! Want
a 1"-by-2" or a
2"-by-3"?
Just split a
pole, twist
the froe
and with
three more
rives
you're got it!

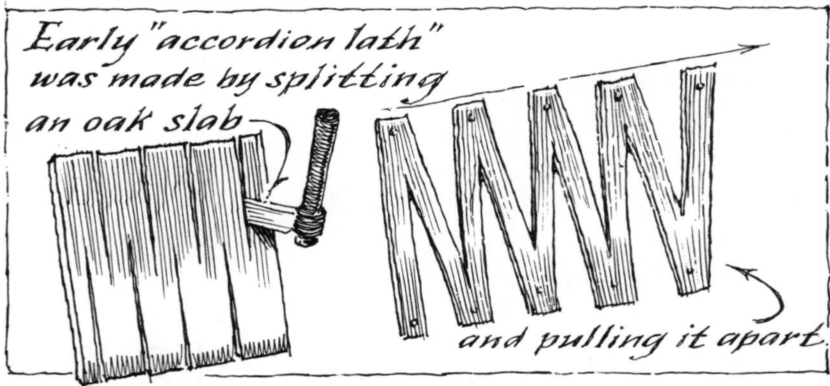
Early "accordion lath"
was made by splitting
an oak slab
and pulling it apart

a rare froe is the Knife Froe
14"
All wrought metal . . . New Hampshire about 1740

Tools with Legs

Chairmaking was one of the earliest industries of the Shakers, so it is natural that they were also pioneers in installing their wonderful mechanical appliances onto benches so that operators could sit while working. The first American shingle bench may have been made in Maine or Pennsylvania, but it reached its peak in design with the Shakers.

One Lebanon (New York) shinglemaker filled a request for 5,000 shingles in December of 1789, which, apparently, was a usual sort of output for one operator. Shaker-made broom-vices, apple parers, nail-benches, and herb-cutters were installed on legs and attached to stools of one kind or another or designed so that the buyer could affix the appliance to a bench he made himself. To sit at work was, all of a sudden, a new American pleasure.

a Chair Vise

an Apple Quarterer

To Sit at your Work . . .

The American Horse

The American saw-horse is now usually carpenter-made and hastily knocked together by the workman to be discarded "after the job is done"; it can also be bought ready-made, put together with "two-by-fours" and metal fasteners. Either way the modern saw-horse is more a temporary prop than a well-designed table. The early saw-horse, which had a flat top, was wide enough to hold the wood being sawed and other things too; it was usually a handy and permanent part of the tool room.

An Early American sawyer's prop was made of two clubs pushed against a raised log. A later arrangement was the "tackle prop," a stick pushed through a forked bough; two of these could hold a whole log in place.

The first "saw-buck" was a tripod (a tilted cross with a stick through it) and it was called a "saw-goat" instead of a "saw-buck" (the Dutch word *zaag-boc* means saw-goat). So the three-legged *zaag-boc* became our four-legged saw-buck!

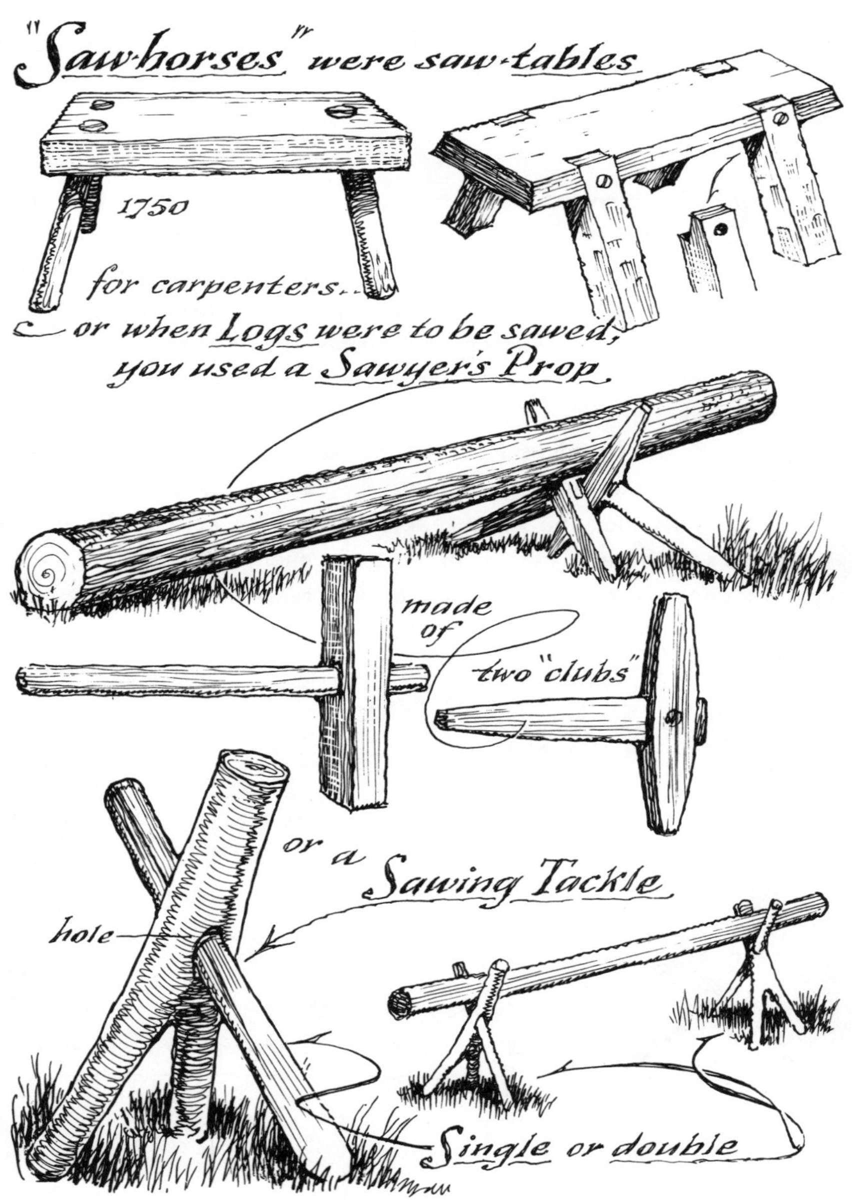
"Saw-horses" were saw-tables
1750
for carpenters...
or when Logs were to be sawed,
you used a Sawyer's Prop
made of
two "clubs"
or a
Sawing Tackle
hole
Single or double

"For Making 'Snitzels'"

First called the "drawing knife" because you drew it toward you, the drawknife (or snitzel-knife, as some Pennsylvanians called it) came to America before the Pilgrims. But only with the emergence of the snitzel-bank, or shaving horse, which made it simpler to hold the article being shaved, did the drawknife become a most favored tool. There are probably more ancient drawknives extant than any other antique tool.

The drawknife was used to taper the sides of shingles, to rough-size the edges of floor boards and rough-trim paneling before planing them, to fashion axe, rake, and other tool handles, and to make stool legs, ox yokes, pump handles, and wheel spokes. It is easy to see why the drawknife was so popular! The final finishing on much drawknife work was done by our next tool, the spokeshave and scraper.

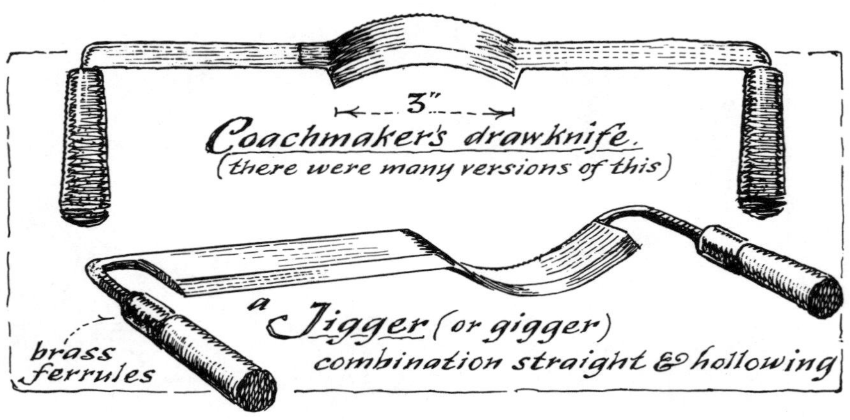

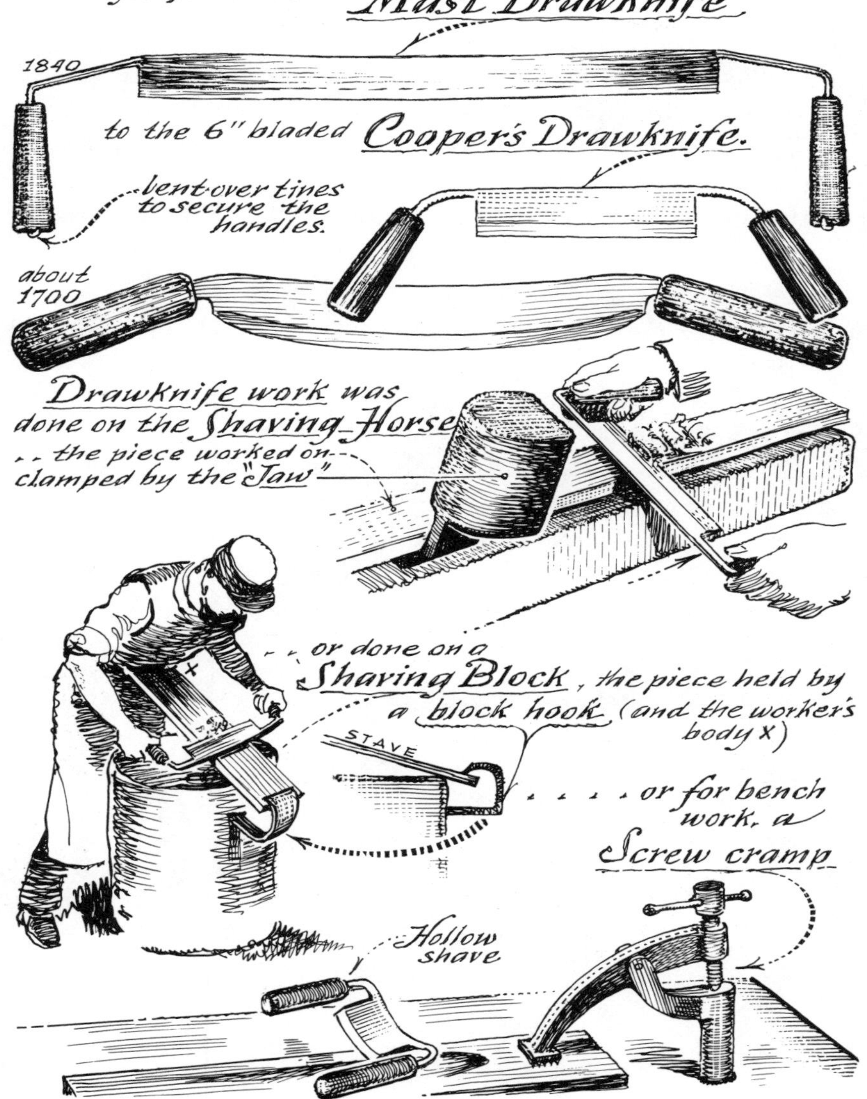
The Drawknife first called Draft Shave
ranged from the 24" Mast Drawknife
1840
to the 6" bladed Cooper's Drawknife.
bent-over tines to secure the handles.
about 1700
Drawknife work was done on the Shaving Horse
.. the piece worked on clamped by the "Jaw"
.. or done on a Shaving Block, the piece held by a block hook (and the worker's body X)
STAVE
.... or for bench work, a Screw cramp
Hollow shave

Little Shavers and Big

The difference between the drawknife and its little brother the spokeshave is like the difference between the old open razor and the safety razor. The spokeshave has a regulated depth of cut. Tap the tangs and the cut deepens; tap the face of the blade back and it becomes more shallow. Often a screw held the adjustment in place. All-metal spokeshaves appeared just before the Civil War; before that, the variety of wood handles seems endless.

The biggest shaver was the chamfer knife, sometimes all metal, which is often misrepresented (even by the experts) as a kind of froe. The sharp upper surface, however, shows that it was not designed for striking; and the curve-beveled blade is certainly not for splitting.

Although the tiny tools shown below were called "top and side shaves," they were really planes. They were designed for the use of stairmakers, but coachmakers found them even more useful.

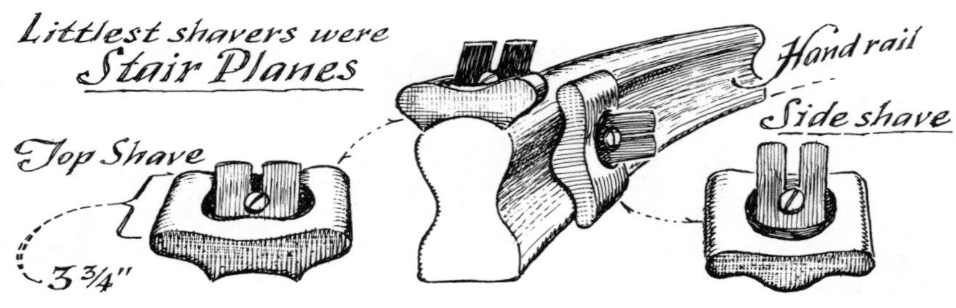

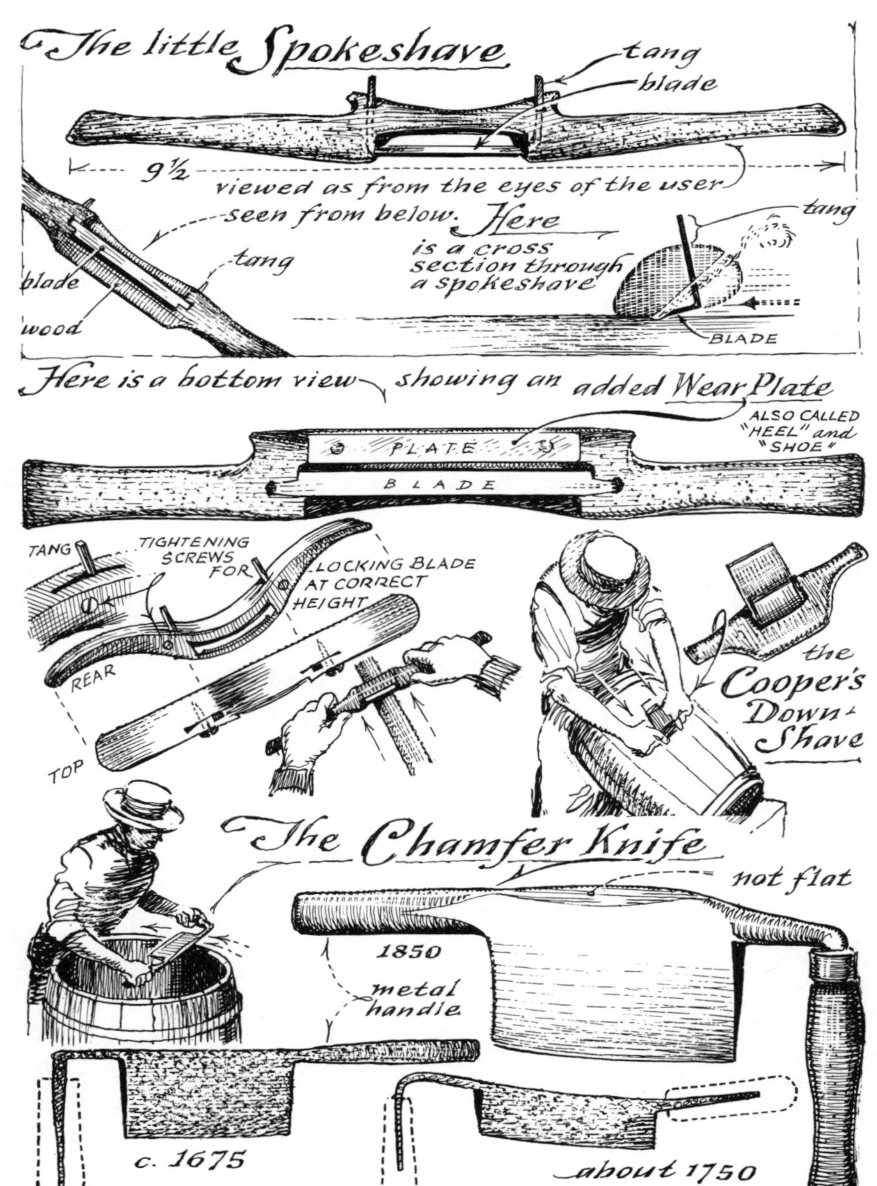
The little Spokeshave
tang
blade
9½
viewed as from the eyes of the user
seen from below. Here
is a cross section through a spokeshave
tang
blade
tang
wood
BLADE
Here is a bottom view showing an added Wear Plate
ALSO CALLED "HEEL" and "SHOE"
PLATE
BLADE
TANG
TIGHTENING SCREWS FOR
LOCKING BLADE AT CORRECT HEIGHT
REAR
TOP
the Cooper's Down-Shave
The Chamfer Knife
not flat
1850
metal handle
c. 1675
about 1750

The Days of River Rafting

In many wooded areas of eighteenth-century America, farmers raised crops mostly for their own use and derived cash only from the sale of wood. Timber was floated to its destination by means of fastening logs into giant rafts. Three or more "platforms" were fastened, one behind the other, to make one long raft; steering was done by long oars. When rafts were sold and dismantled at the mill, irons and fastening devices were put into kegs, loaded on wagons, and hauled back to the farm. Most farmers ran at least one raft a year in late winter (when rivers were high) and busied themselves a good part of each winter with making or repairing lumbering implements.

White pine for masts and spars was a prime American export in the early 1800's and up until the Civil War. On such rivers as the Delaware were floated more than a thousand rafts each spring. The largest one on record was 215 feet long, and it contained 120,000 feet of lumber.

Below is a device known as a "bow-and-pin fastener." The square pins were driven into holes in the log; the wooden bow held the lash pole in place.

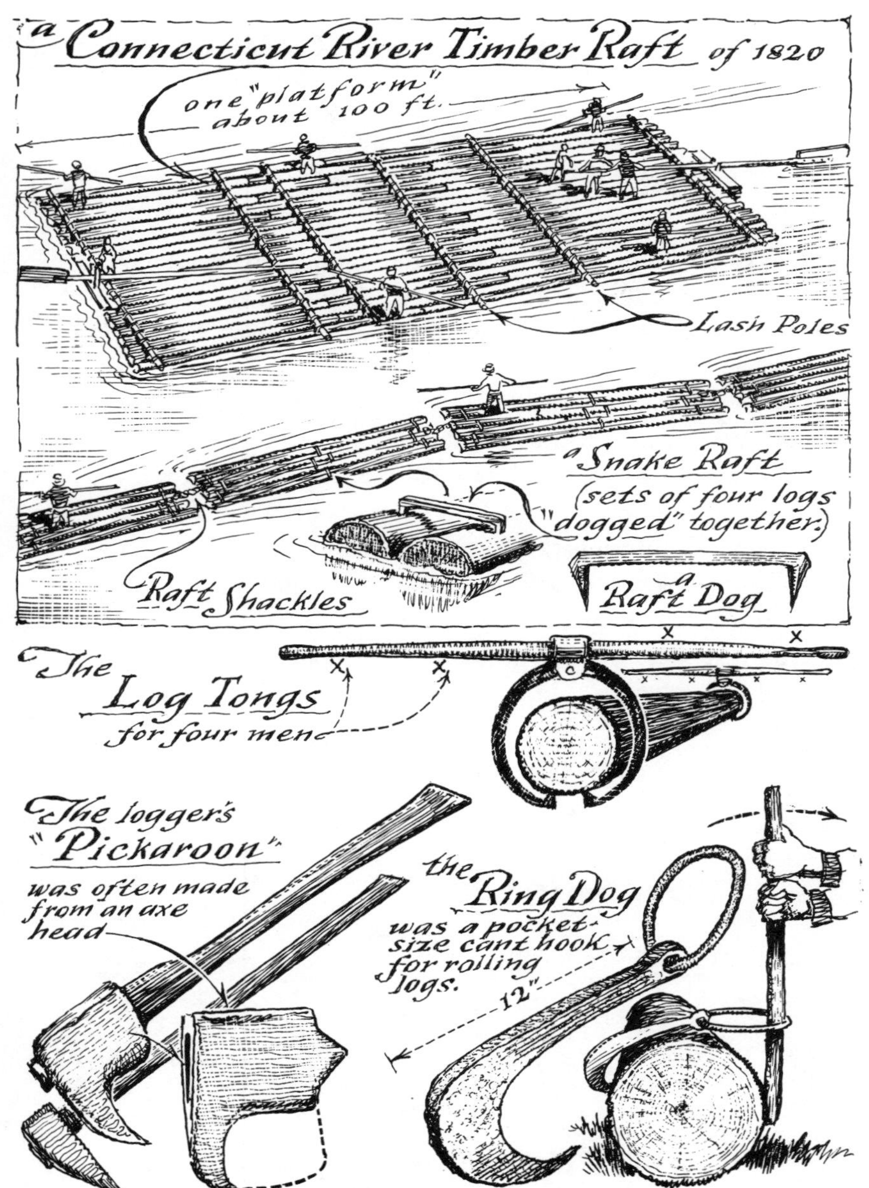
a Connecticut River Timber Raft of 1820
one "platform" about 100 ft.
Lash Poles
a Snake Raft (sets of four logs "dogged" together.)
Raft Shackles
a Raft Dog
The Log Tongs for four men
The logger's "Pickaroon" was often made from an axe head
the Ring Dog was a pocket-size cant hook for rolling logs.
12"

Tools of the River Lumberman

The American word "lumberman" came before our present use of the word lumber. "Lumber" at one time (and still does in England) meant "anything useless or cumbersome."

The so-called "ship augers" you find in antique shops had not, as you might think, anything to do with ships; they were really used for log-rafts, or log-ships. The length of these augers allowed a man to bore a hole while standing.

The lash-pole and wooden-pin method of building rafts was later replaced by iron raft shackles and "dogs."

Loose logs were "herded" into "corrals" by the owners at the mill (branded with the owners' marks). The marking axe was also an inspection axe with a special bark-lifting poll.

Below you may see how the cant hook was made (in 1870 by a blacksmith named John Peavey) into the "American peavey" by wedding it to the jam pike. The jam pike pried, the cant hook rolled, but the peavey did both.

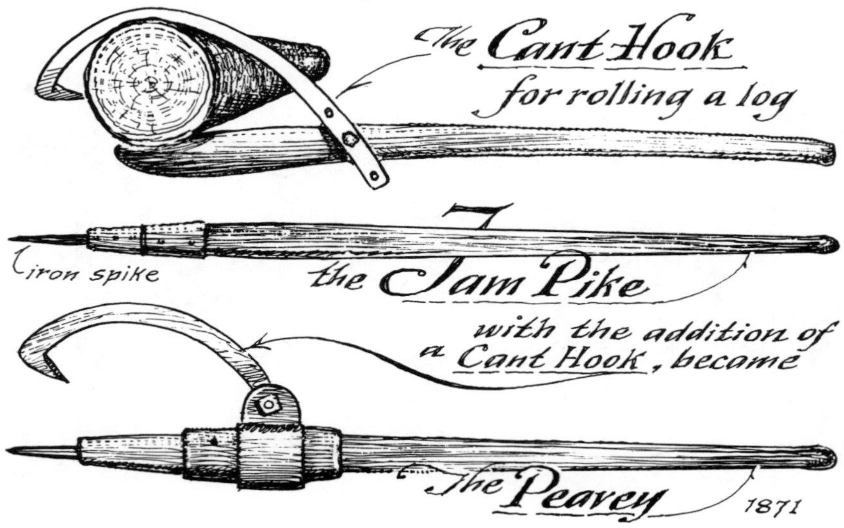
The Cant Hook
for rolling a log
iron spike
the Jam Pike
with the addition of
a Cant Hook, became
The Peavey
1871

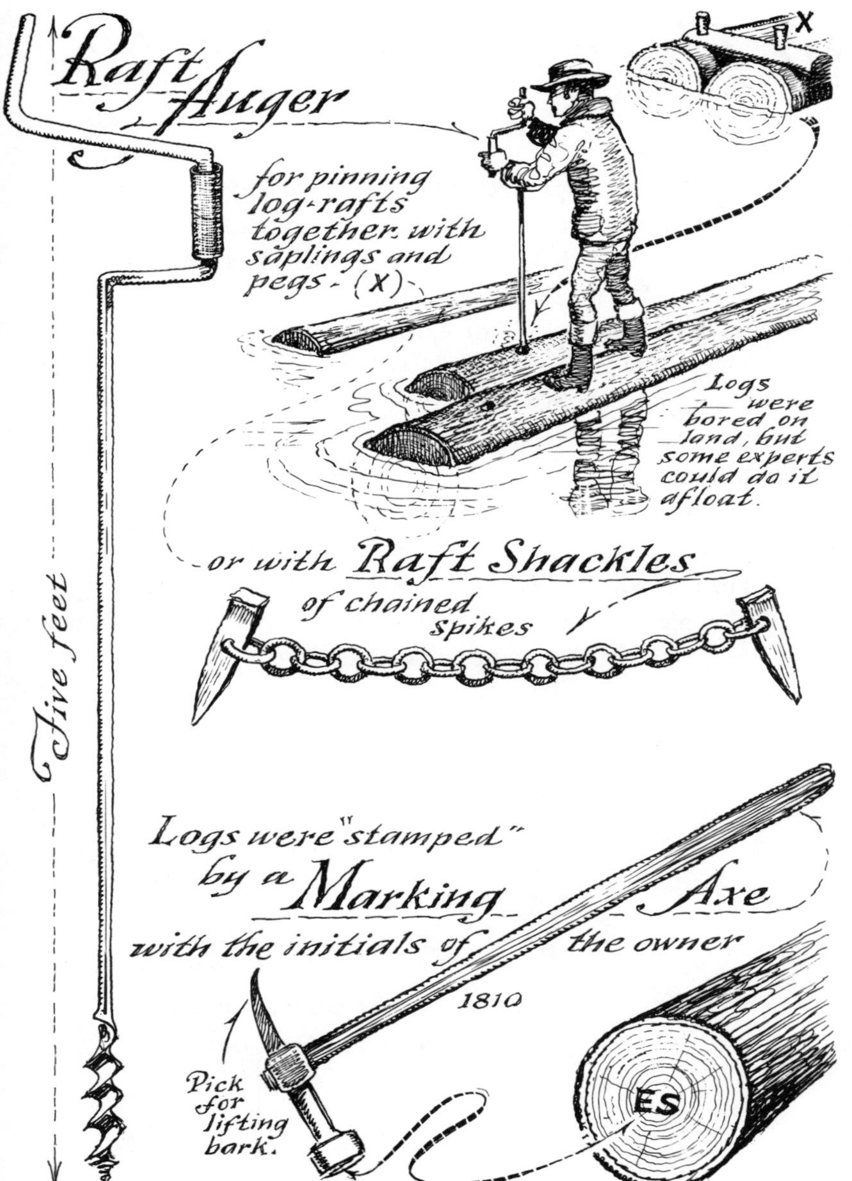
Raft Auger
for pinning log-rafts together with saplings and pegs - (X)
X
Logs were bored on land, but some experts could do it afloat.
Five feet
or with Raft Shackles
of chained spikes
Logs were "stamped" by a Marking Axe
with the initials of the owner
1810
Pick for lifting bark.
ES

Of Cider and Apple Butter

Anything that touched apples, according to the old way of thinking, had to be made of wood. Even a nail would "risk spoiling the flavor" or "quicken a souring." So heavy treen-ware (appliances and tools made from trees) was necessary in the apple industry.

Cider was never a matter of just squeezing—there was a special art to "bruising" apples and leaving them exposed to air for a certain and exact time before pressing. Oddly, those who picked eating apples carefully from the tree to avoid bumping them made an elaborate ceremony of crushing the same fruit when making cider.

Apples were never squeezed: "pomace was pressed." A mash was made into pomace or "cheese," then carefully placed between straw mats so the juice could be pressed out. The pomace rake, apple butter scoop, "cheese cutter," and apple shovel are tools that are difficult to understand now, for they are lost to the times when cider was America's national drink and apple butter the national spread.

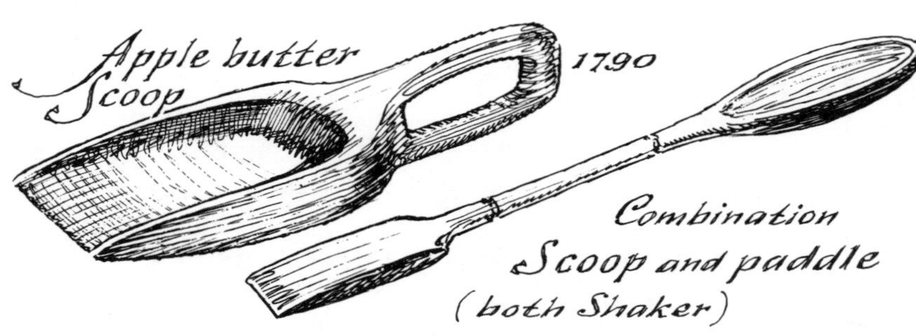

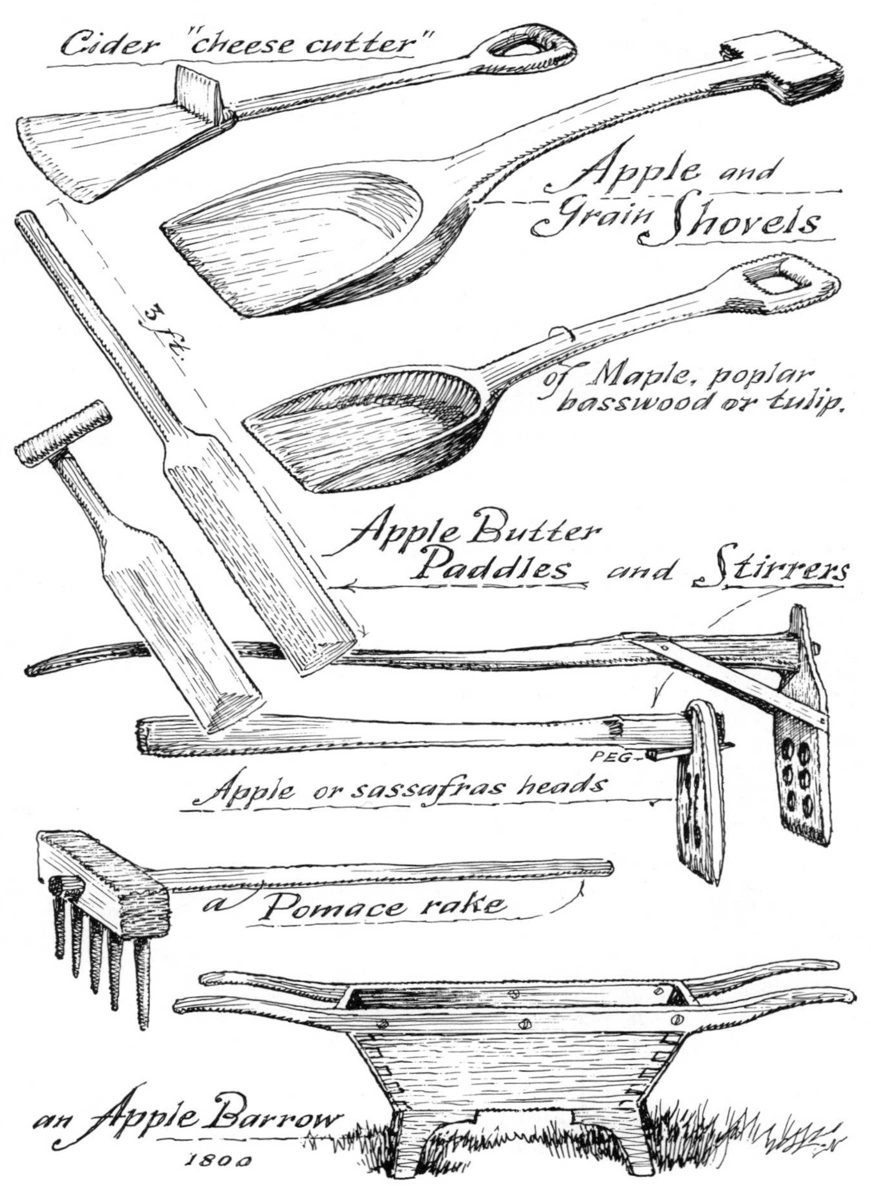
Cider "cheese cutter"
Apple and Grain Shovels
3 ft.
of Maple, poplar basswood or tulip.
Apple Butter Paddles and Stirrers
PEG
Apple or sassafras heads
a Pomace rake
an Apple Barrow
1800

To Remove Bark

Until recently the main source of tannin for treating hides was obtained from oak bark, and the production of oak bark was an essential part of the economy of many American farms. In April and May, bark peeled easily, and this was done with the spud, barking iron, and barking axe. The peeling chisel and adze were used mostly for "debarking" cedar posts and cleaning logs before broad-axing. The irons and spuds were true tanbark tools, usually blacksmith-made to order.

At first, chunks of oak bark were ground under massive stone mill wheels that turned into a trough of stone, but as early as 1797 the iron bark mill entered the scene to create a major American industry.

The liquor for tanning was obtained by pouring cold water on finely ground bark and leaving it to stand for a few days. Then it was passed from one leaching pit to another till the desired strength was reached.

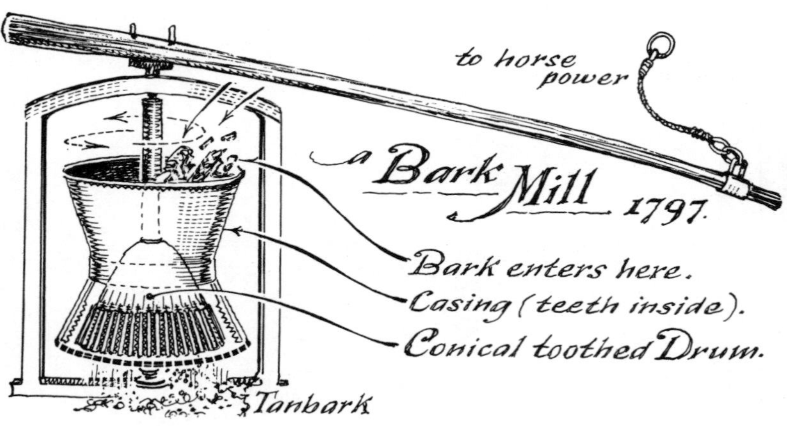

Bark was stripped from logs with the Bark Spud
Stripping to hasten drying of timber wood
NEW ENGLAND C. 1800
NEW YORK 1850
and Peeling Chisel
and Barking Irons for cutting Bark for Tanning
1800's
spoon spud
harvested oak bark
about 1790
The Barking Axe did the ringing
c. 1730
SPUD.
and splitting before the Spud's work
3 FT.

Two Heads are Better than One.

Except for the double-bitted axe, these tools are rare. So rare in fact, that there is doubt about their true names. One of the first dictionary mentions of the "twibil" calls it "an iron tool used by Paviers" (road-builders). This would make it a sort of grubbing hoe. Another describes it as a twin-billed hoe-and-knife for beans and peas. One old dictionary says the "twivel" is "among Carpenters, a tool to make Tortoise Holes." We must assume this definition was dictated to a printer who mistook "mortise" for "tortoise."

I would guess that all two-bitted hatchets might have been at some time called "twin-bills," "twibils," or "twivels." Still used in England to cut hurdle mortises, the twivel there is called "tomyhawk," "dader," or "two-bill."

The ice hatchet, adze-hatchet, and hatchet-adze were American, but only the Yankee double-bit remains. From Maine (about 1840) it was designed with one razor-sharp bit that could do fine work and one less sharp for rough work. It also provides a means for being held (by sinking it into a stump) for filing either bit.

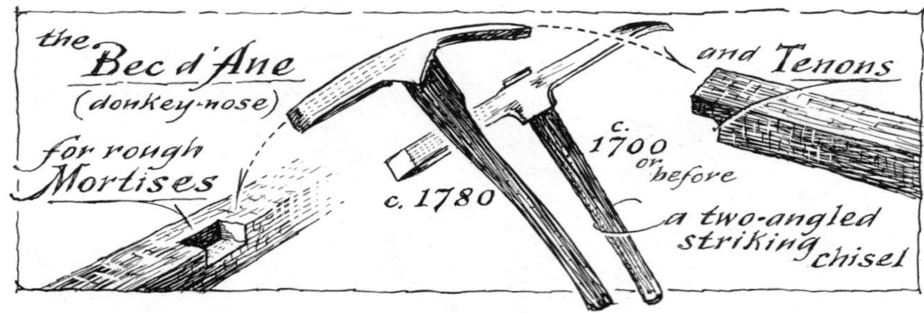

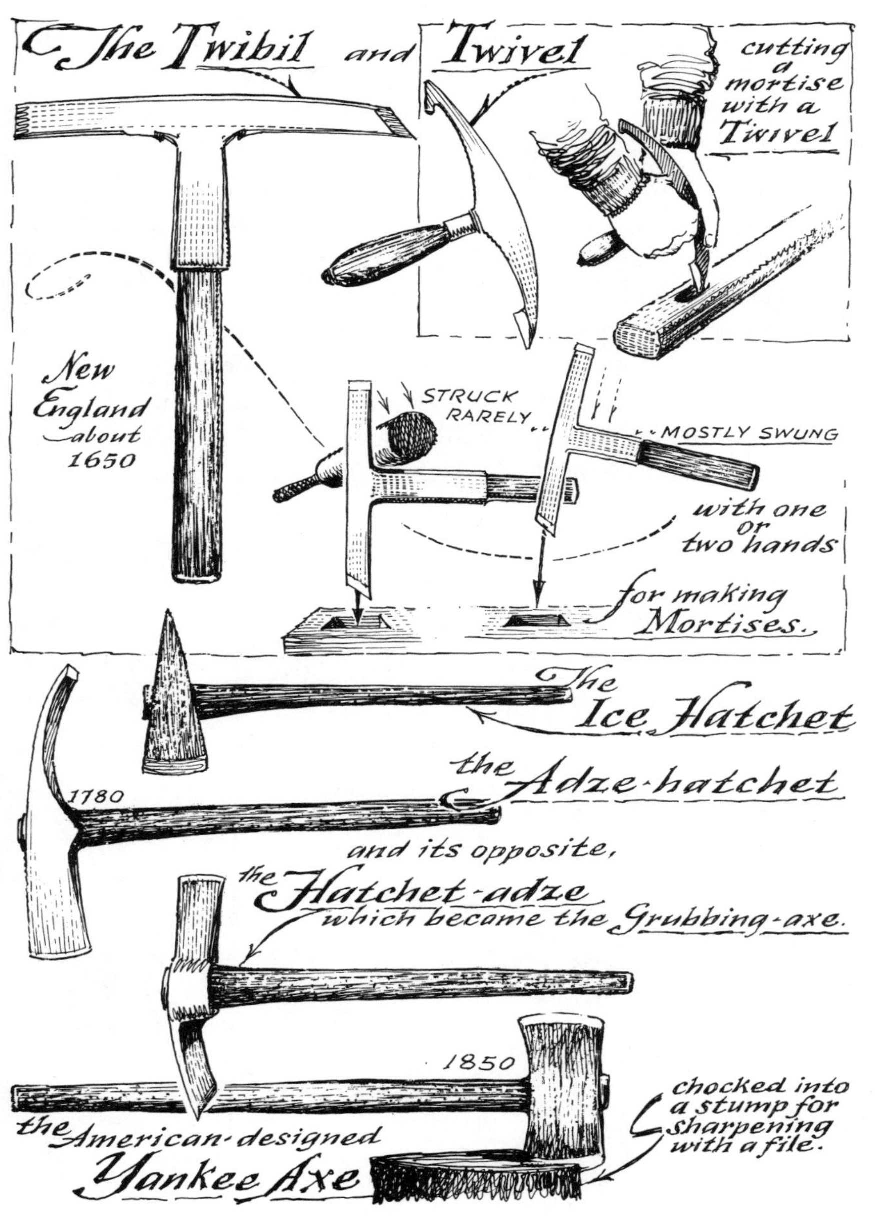
The Twibil and Twivel
cutting a mortise with a Twivel
New England about 1650
STRUCK RARELY
MOSTLY SWUNG
with one or two hands
for making Mortises.
The Ice Hatchet
the Adze-hatchet
1780
and its opposite,
the Hatchet-adze
which became the Grubbing-axe.
1850
the American-designed
Yankee Axe
chocked into a stump for sharpening with a file.

The Chisel

There are so many kinds of chisels that it is difficult to establish definite nomenclature; yet, on the opposite page, we have attempted a general classification. The firmer (or firming or forming) chisel is the basic chisel design; it did a great many jobs, but one special use was to cut the superfluous wood from two auger holes to make a mortise. The framing chisel is a heavier version, and it was used largely in the cutting of tenons to fit the mortises. Both of these tools are wood-handled (usually socketed) and were designed to be struck with a mallet. The socket-end can be struck bare, without the handle, though a good craftsman seldom did this.

The short, stout mortise chisel is almost square, a one-purpose tool. The giant paring chisel, known as a slick, has a big blade that curves very slightly toward the bevel; it was designed, not for striking, but to be used with two hands (often with some shoulder help) like a giant plane. Big framing chisels are often misnamed slicks; if the curve is evident, it is a slick; if not, it is a giant framing chisel.

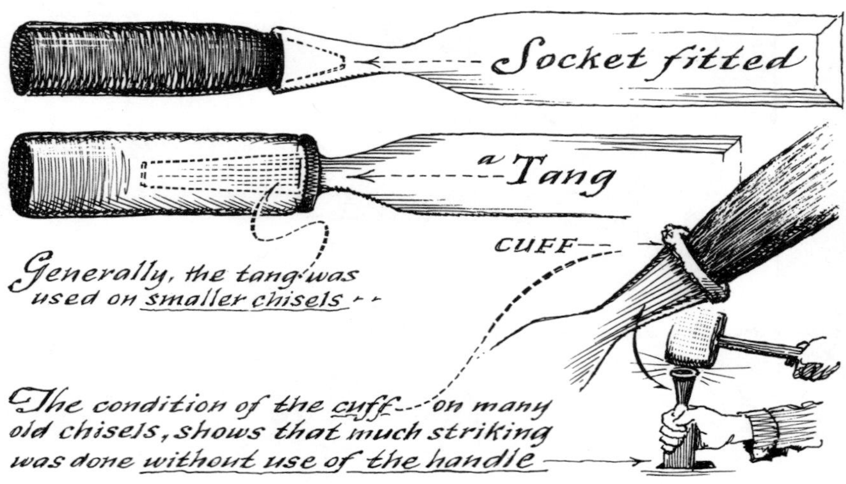

Socket fitted
a Tang
CUFF
Generally, the tang was used on smaller chisels
The condition of the cuff on many old chisels, shows that much striking was done without use of the handle

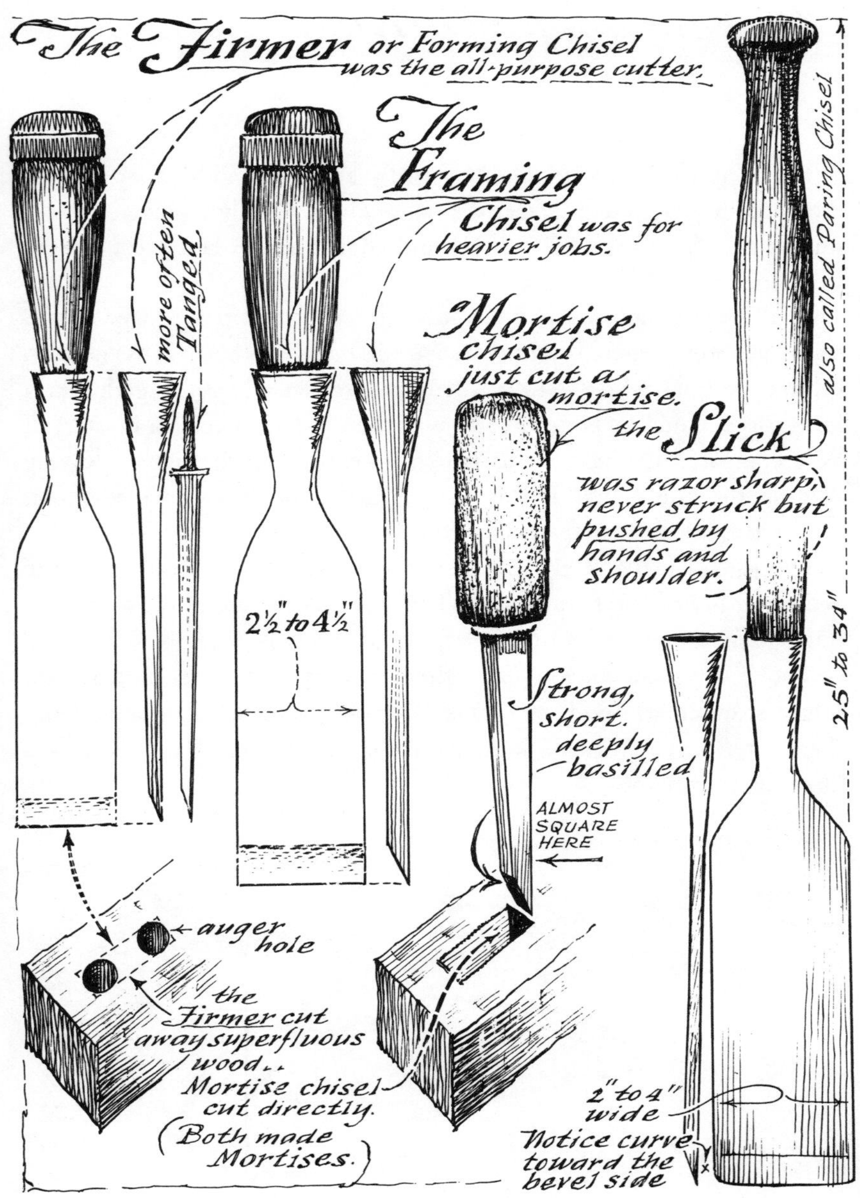
The Firmer or Forming Chisel was the all-purpose cutter.
more often Tanged
The Framing Chisel was for heavier jobs.
2½" to 4½"
a Mortise chisel just cut a mortise.
Strong, short. deeply basilled
ALMOST SQUARE HERE
the Slick
was razor sharp, never struck but pushed by hands and shoulder.
also called Paring Chisel
25" to 34"
2" to 4" wide
Notice curve toward the bevel side
auger hole
the Firmer cut away superfluous wood..
Mortise chisel cut directly.
(Both made Mortises.)

Chisels and Gouges

What many call a "round chisel" is really a "gouge." The story told on the opposite page is that the earliest gouges were usually all metal (blacksmith-made from the Old World) and copied in this country in larger form for use with wooden handles.

The 1775 gouge in the illustration has an interesting story. It was found in a stone fence. Bright and silverish, its edge is keen; it has no rust. How farm-bound bog iron, privately smelted, hammered together at a farm forge, could be better in any way than today's steel is a mystery. I have compared the best chisels (the most expensive, that is) by leaving them in the rain alongside this ancient tool. The new tool's edge was dulled, and rust appeared within a few days.

The legend is that early surface ore contained much manganese and was purer in iron content. It is also believed that the use of charcoal gave purer carbon content and made a superior iron.

The chisels shown below had individual uses; some were used as bark scrapers, others as beam smoothers (like big planes). But I cannot find them listed or catalogued. Some ice chisels are similar, but they lack a tilted bit (see below—*x*).

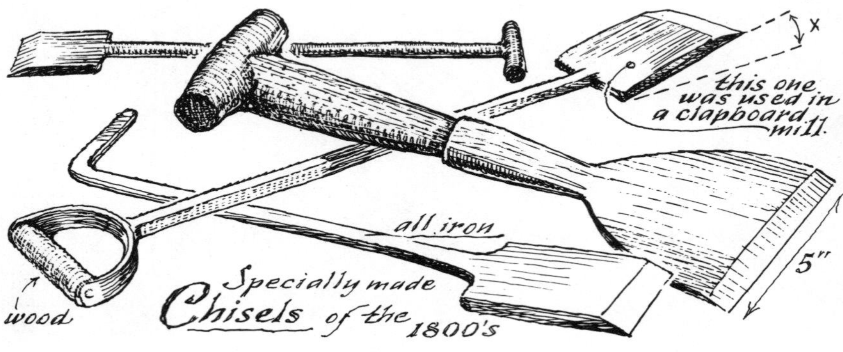

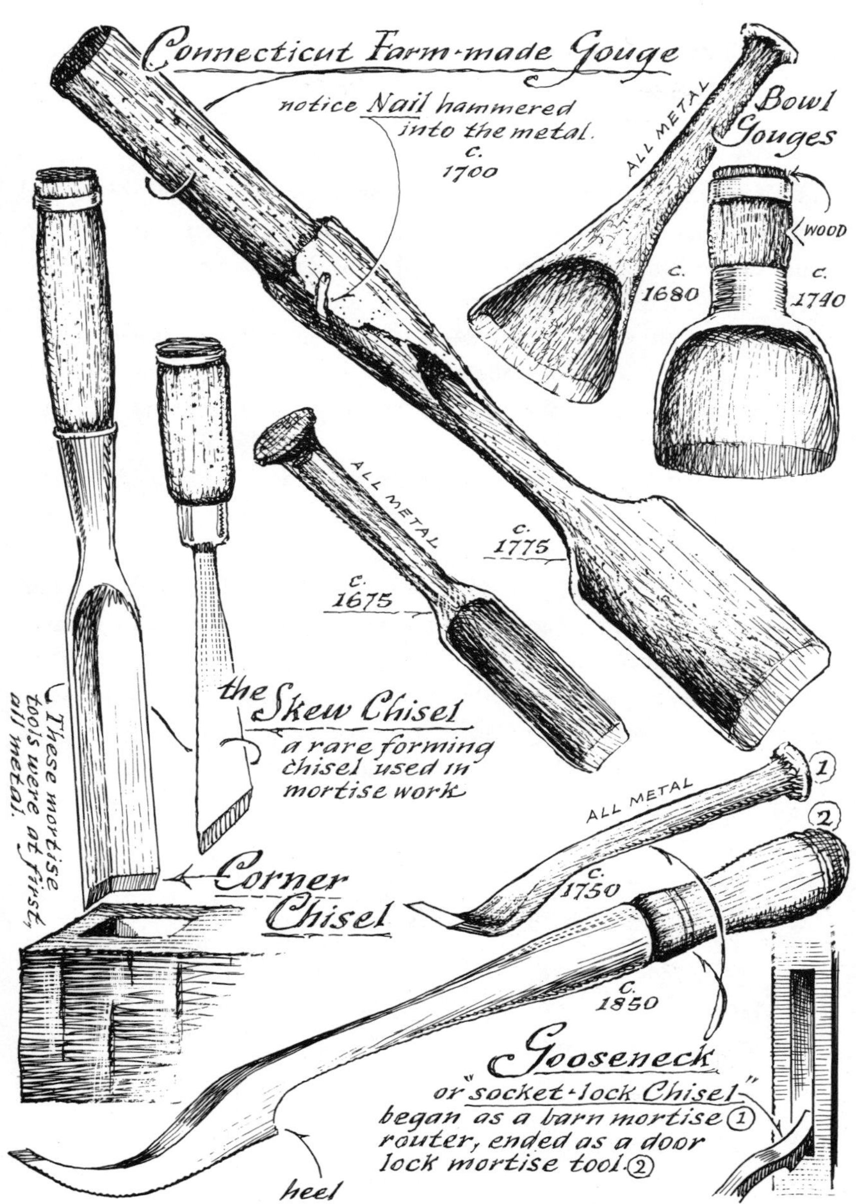
Connecticut Farm-made Gouge
notice Nail hammered into the metal.
c. 1700
ALL METAL
Bowl Gouges
WOOD
c. 1680
c. 1740
ALL METAL
c. 1775
c. 1675
These mortise tools were at first all metal.
the Skew Chisel
a rare forming chisel used in mortise work
ALL METAL
1
2
c. 1750
Corner Chisel
c. 1850
Gooseneck
or "socket-lock Chisel"
began as a barn mortise router, ended as a door lock mortise tool.
heel

Planes

Old World planes, made as much to look at as to do a job, often had inscriptions and floral carving. But the completely utilitarian American plane, except for an occasional graceful handle, usually resembled a box. Looking alike, a nest of small planes in the average carpenter's chest often reached thirty or more. Perhaps because of their plainness, or their quantity, they never caught the collector's fancy. Not long ago in Vermont, you could buy them by the barrel as firewood for five dollars. That included the barrel!

From the big ones ("long" planes) down, these either leveled the surface or fit pieces (side by side) together. Leveling was called "trying" and "trueing"; fitting was called "jointing."

With the trying plane (top, opposite) was a smaller bench plane called a jack plane and a larger (now rare) mate, the long jointer, or floor plane. But all other planes bow to their granddaddy in size, the cooper's long jointer, which was used upside down on a pair of legs to work the piece. Restricted in use mostly to joining barrel staves, this plane sometimes had two blades—one for rough, one for fine cut.

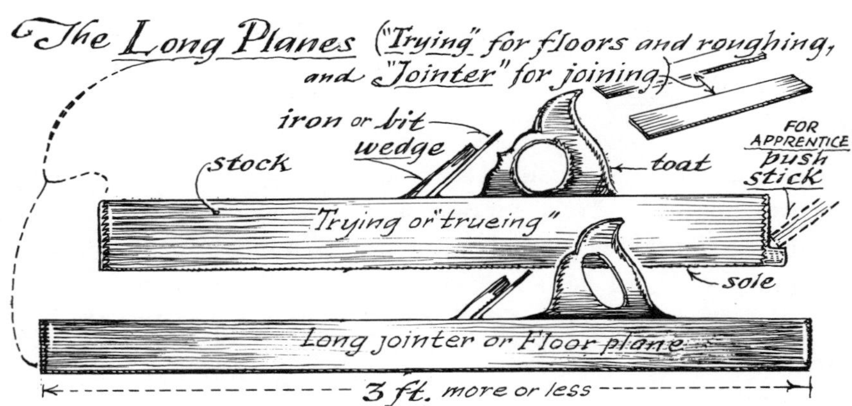

Here are some general dimensions

Names of Planes	length	width	iron width
Modelling Plane	1" to 5"	1/4" to 2"	3/16" to 1 1/2"
Smoothing Plane	6" to 8"	2 1/2" to 3 1/2"	1 3/4" to 2 3/8"
Rabbet Plane	9 1/2"	3/8" to 2"	3/8" to 2"
Jack Plane	12" to 17"	2 1/2 to 3"	2" to 2 1/4"
Long or Trying Plane	20" to 26"	3 1/2"	2 1/2" to 2 5/8"
Jointer Plane or Floor Plane	28" to 36"	3 3/4"	2 3/4"
Cooper's long jointer	60" to 72"	5" to 5 1/2"	3 1/2" to 3 3/4"

The Moulding Plane

The grandest plane was the crown moulding plane. That large strip between the wall and ceiling was the identification of a fine room as well as the mark of the craftsman. No workman even carried about so large a tool and few owned one; instead the ordinary workman improvised with the basic "hollow" and "round" planes to make a moulding that the crown could do at one sweep.

The big crown plane was so heavy that it had bars for the apprentice to pull it by rope (1). Or, looped once or twice around a mill-wheel shaft (2), it could be pulled by tightening the rope, released by loosening.

Some crown planes had an apprentice pulling stick (3); others had a bar screwed across the front of the stock (4); others had two bars that slid into the front and back of the stock (5), with a notch for a second apprentice to push by stick.

The simplest moulding plane made a bead, but even this design came in sets of eight (from an eighth of an inch to a full inch), so you can see how a well-equipped carpenter's chest often had twenty or more moulding planes.

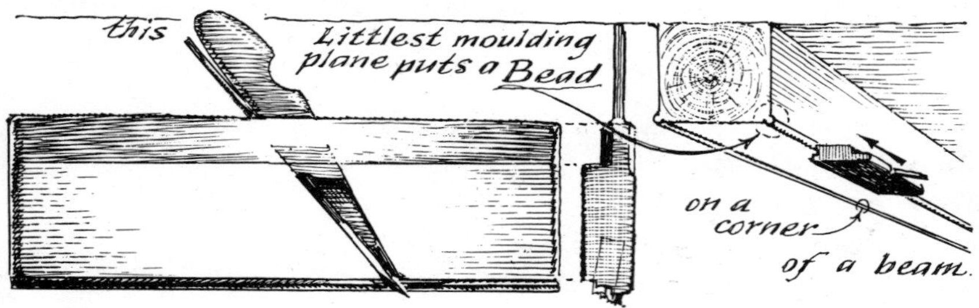

this
Littlest moulding plane puts a Bead
on a corner of a beam.

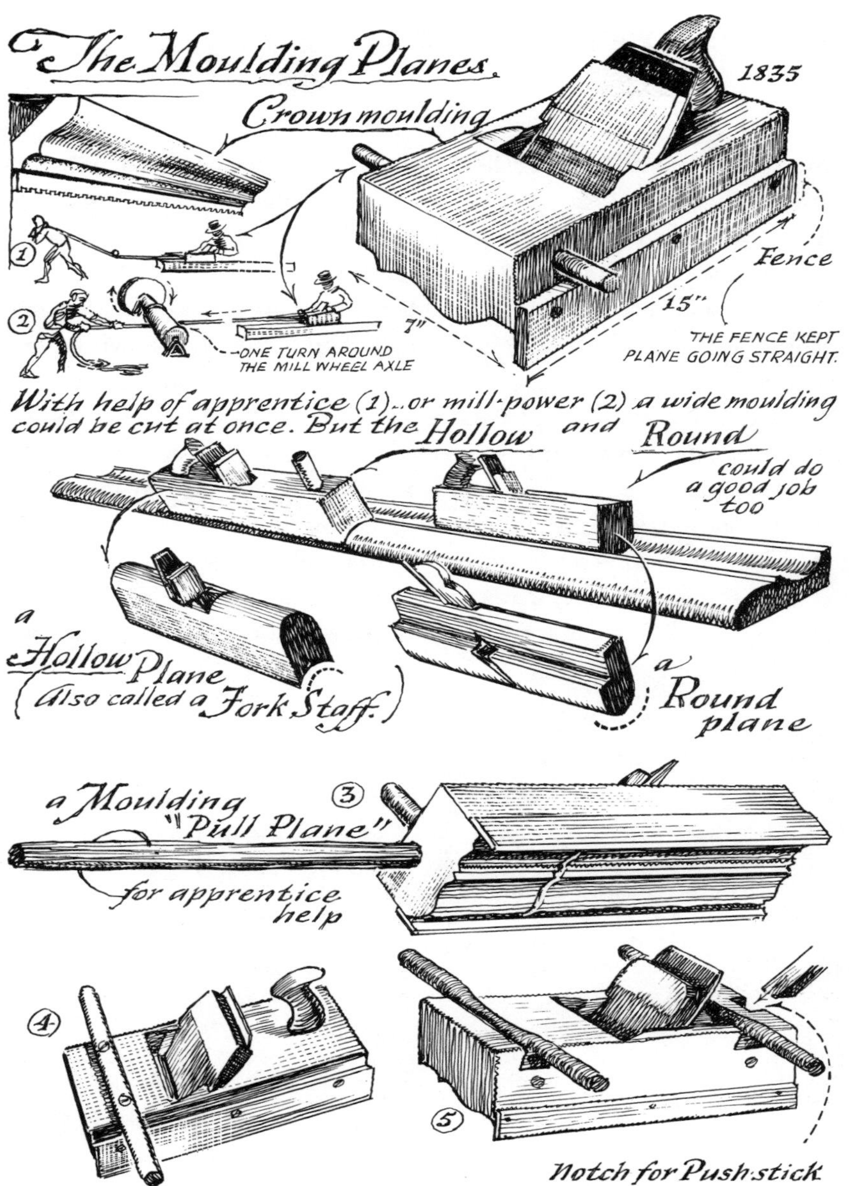
The Moulding Planes
1835
Crown moulding
Fence
15"
7"
THE FENCE KEPT PLANE GOING STRAIGHT.
ONE TURN AROUND THE MILL WHEEL AXLE
1
2
With help of apprentice (1)...or mill-power (2) a wide moulding could be cut at once. But the Hollow and Round could do a good job too
a Hollow Plane (Also called a Fork Staff.)
a Round plane
a Moulding "Pull Plane" for apprentice help
3
4
5
Notch for Push-stick

The Rabbet

Most American carpenters call it a "rabbit"; the British call it a "rebate." It is really the "rabbet plane" that "rabbets" out a cut in the sides of boards, so that they may be overlapped and joined. This was the popular way of joining before milled tongue-and-groove.

The first rabbet and the long rabbet plane have fences (overlapping strips) to guide the plane along the end of the board (as shown on the opposite page). Because the little rabbet stands flat without a fence, it needs a strip of wood nailed along its route to guide it before it can properly cut a rabbet in a board.

These planes vary in design, some throwing shavings to the right, some to the left, some to both sides. Some irons have blades set, instead of at a right angle, on a skew to the stock to avoid tearing the wood. Rarer is the pistol-grip-handled rabbet, which lacks the usual wedge for holding the iron. Below is the rabbet saw, rarely used except in stairmaking.

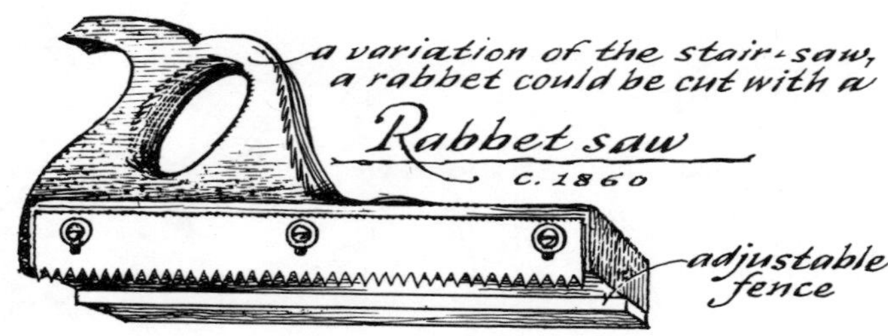
a variation of the stair-saw,
a rabbet could be cut with a
Rabbet saw
c. 1860
adjustable fence

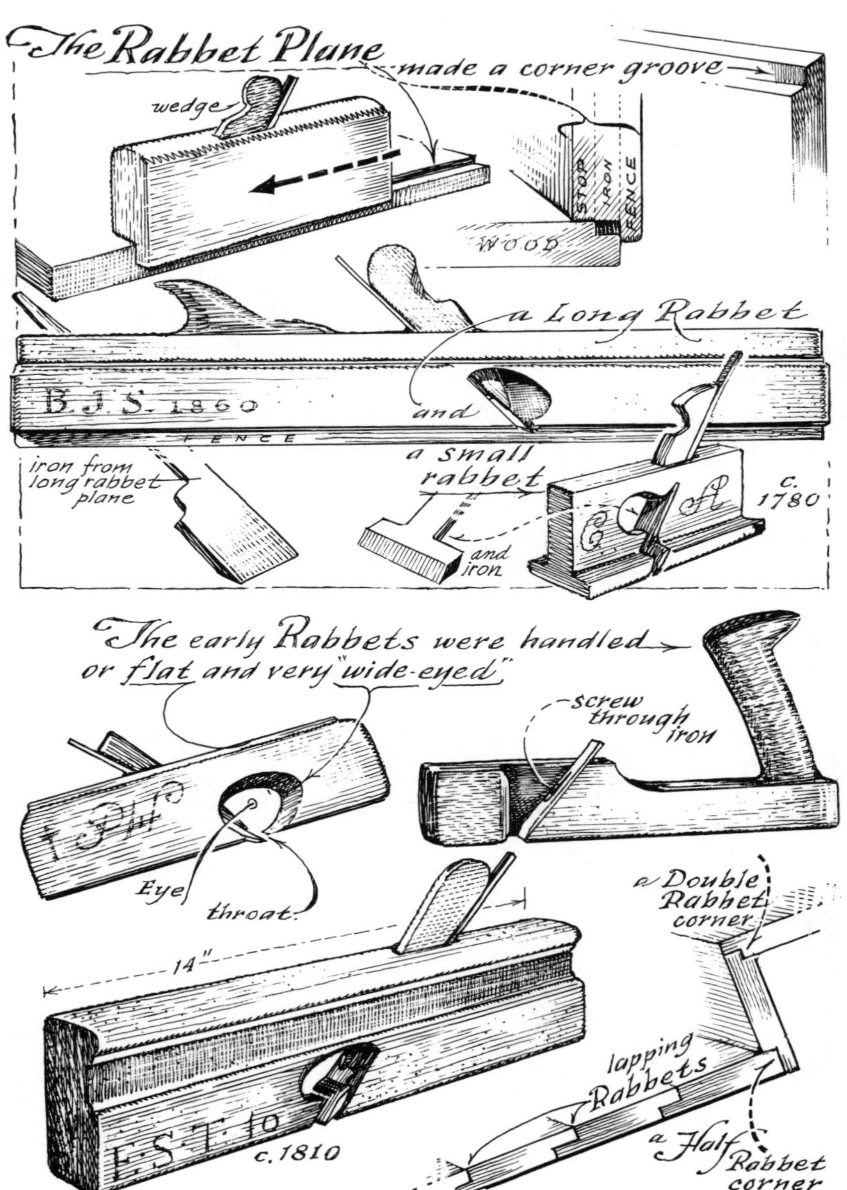
The Rabbet Plane
made a corner groove
wedge
STOP
IRON
FENCE
WOOD
a Long Rabbet
B.J.S. 1860
FENCE
and
iron from long rabbet plane
a small rabbet
and iron
c. 1780
The early Rabbets were handled or flat and very "wide-eyed"
screw through iron
Eye
throat
14"
E.S.T. 10
c.1810
a Double Rabbet corner
lapping Rabbets
a Half Rabbet corner

The Plow

The plow plane did the simplest job, yet it looks like the most complicated of tools. It just makes a groove. We use tongue-and-groove cuts for flooring and sheathing without realizing how recent this practice is. Before the "tongue" was popular, two grooves were placed against each other, and a "spline" was driven into the "tunnel" to join the two pieces together. For paneling, a tongue was not planed, but a "feather edge" was set into the groove.

The adjustable plow had its fence attached to the plane by two arms that slid through the plane stock and made secure by wooden wedges. Later the square arms became two long round screws with threaded knobs to hold them secure.

The unadjustable plow and unadjustable tongue plane came in pairs ("tongue-and-groove sets"), and there was also a combination of the two, set into one stock (see following pages).

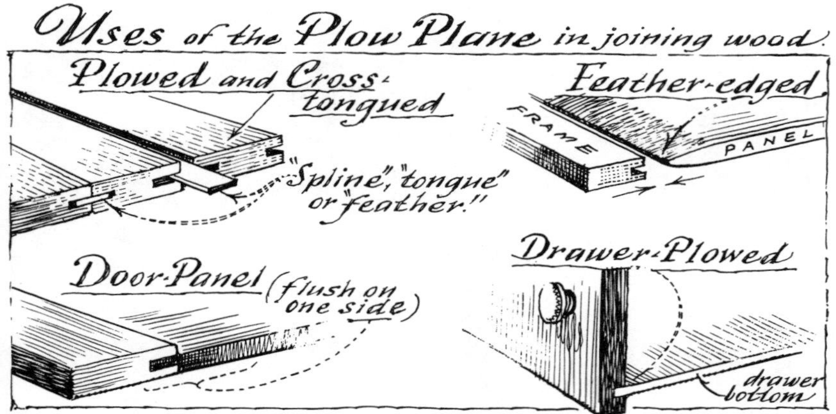

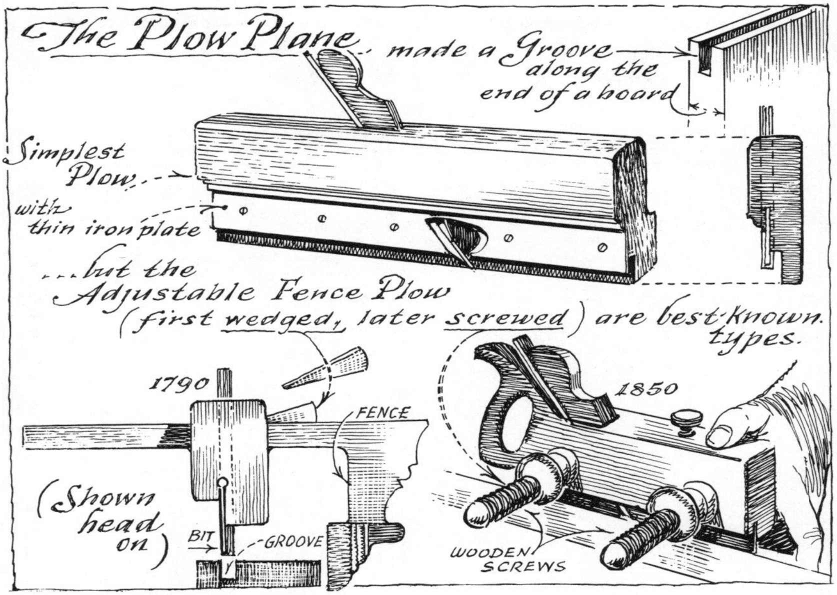

The Plow Plane ... made a Groove along the end of a board

Simplest Plow

with thin iron plate

...but the Adjustable Fence Plow (first wedged, later screwed) are best-known types.

1790

FENCE

(Shown head on)

BIT

GROOVE

1850

WOODEN SCREWS

The Adjustable Plow as seen from below.

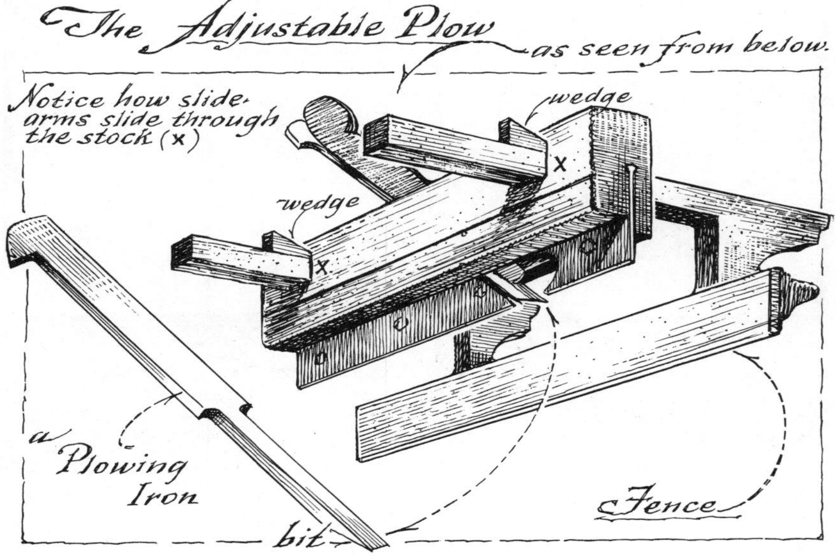

PLANES,

FOR

CARPENTERS, COOPERS, CABINET AND COACH MAKERS.

	CAST STEEL. IRONS. Single.	CAST STEEL. IRONS. Double.	GERMAN STEEL. IRONS. Single.	GERMAN STEEL. IRONS. Double.
Jointers 30 inch	$1 70	$2 17	$1 58	$2 05
do 28 "	1 64	2 08	1 52	1 96
do 26 "	1 58	2 00	1 46	1 88
do 22 "	1 50	1 92	1 38	1 80
do 21 "	1 42	1 84	1 30	1 72
Jack Planes	96	1 37½	88	1 30
Smooth Planes	87½	1 25	80	1 17
do Circular	92	1 31	84	1 23

	CAST STEEL. IRONS. Single.	CAST STEEL. IRONS. Double.	GERMAN STEEL. IRONS. Single.	GERMAN STEEL. IRONS. Double.
Cooper's Jointers	$2 50	$3 50	$2 88	$3 88
do stock howel	2 50	pl'd 3 00	2 38	2 88
do circ. leveler	1 50	" 2 00	1 38	1 87
do with handles	2 00	2 50	1 88	2 38
do crows	2 50			
Tooth Planes	1 25			
Miter Planes	1 00			

Ogees for Cabinet Makers, $1 00 per inch.

Astragals ¼ to ½ inch	62½
do ⅝ to 1 inch	75
Beads ⅛ to ¾ inch	75
do over 1 inch	87½
do full boxed ⅛ to ⅜	92
do do ½ to ¾	1 00
Coves to ¾ inch	62½
do ⅞ to 1 inch	75
Cove and Beads ⅜ to ½ inch	75
do do ⅝ to 1 inch	87½
do do over 1 inch	1 00
Center Beads to ⅜	87
Dadoes, slide stop	1 37
do screw stop	2 00
Fillisters	1 50
do with stop	1 75
do do and cut	2 00
do do cut and boxed	2 25
do with screw stop, cut and boxed	3 00
Guages	20
do oval head	25
Gothic Beads	1 25
Grecian Ovolos ⅜ by ¾ inch	1 00
do do ½ by 1 inch, ⅝ by 1¼	1 12½
do do ¾ by 1½ inch	1 25
do do Beads ⅜ by ⅞ in., ½ by 1⅛ in.	1 25
do do do ⅝ by 1⅜.—¾ by 1¼ in.	1 50
do do do ⅞ by 1¾ and 2 inch	1 75
do Ogee and Bevel sq. ⅜ by ⅞ in. ½ by 1⅛ in.	1 25
do do do ⅝ by 1⅜ in. ¾ by 1½? in.	1 50
do do do ⅞ by 1¾ and 2 inch	1 75
Halving planes	62½
do do plated	87½
do do with handles	1 00
do do plated, with handles	1 25
Hollows and Rounds 9 pair to No. 18.	10 50
Match Planes for Boards ⅝ to 1 inch	1 75
do fence plated	2 00
do for Plank 1¼ inch	2 62½

Match Planes, fence plated	3 00
do moving fence	4 00
do screw arms	6 00
Plows, 1st rate, 8 irons	7 00
do 2d " "	6 00
do 3d " "	5 00
do 4th " "	4 50
Extra for boxing fence	50
Extra for side screws	50
do screw arms and 8 irons	7 00
do box fence	7 50
do side screws	8 00
do solid box	8 00
do do side screws	8 50
Rabbet Planes to 1 inch square 62, skew	75
do 1¼ inch 68, skew	87½
do 1½ inch 75, skew	92
do 1¾ inch 78, skew	1 00
do 2 inch	1 12½
do with handles	2 00
Extra for boxing	25
Extra for adding cut	25
Raising Planes, common	1 75
do moving fence	3 25
do do 3 in. iron	4 00
do do 3½ "	4 50
do do 4 "	5 00
Reeding Planes ⅛ to ½ inch	1 00
Sash Planes, 1 iron 1 00, boxed	1 50
do 2 " 1 50, "	2 00
do double 2 50, "	3 00
Snipe Bills	75
do full box	1 00
Side Rabbets	62½
Torus Beads to ¾ inch	75
do from ¾ to 1 inch	87½
do over 1 inch	1 00
Table Planes, pair	1 50
do boxed	2 00

Omitting various moulding planes and special planes (such as those illustrated on the opposite page), the above advertisement of the 1800's lists some of the basic planes that the average carpenter was likely to have in his chest. As many of these planes came in sets of eight, the army of old-time wooden planes seems overwhelming.

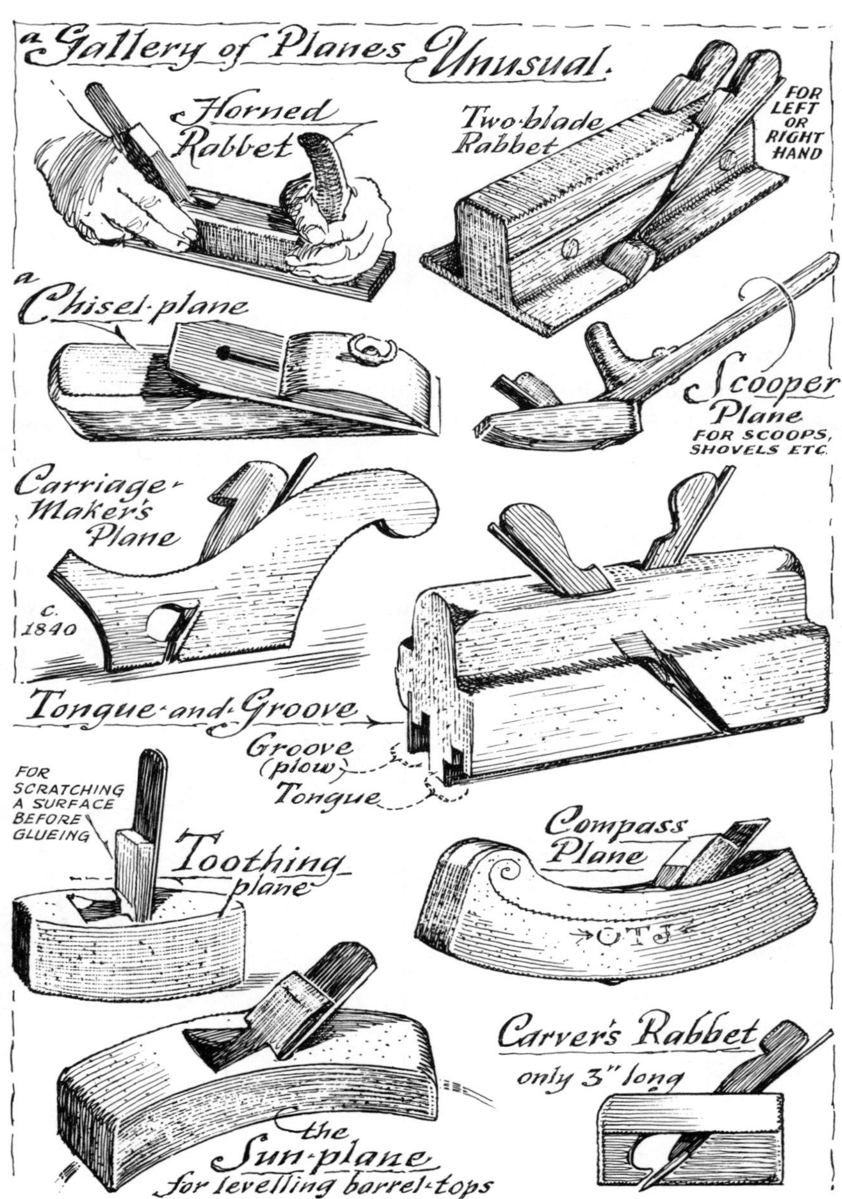
a Gallery of Planes Unusual.
Horned Rabbet
Two-blade Rabbet
FOR LEFT OR RIGHT HAND
a Chisel-plane
Scooper Plane
FOR SCOOPS, SHOVELS ETC.
Carriage-Maker's Plane
c. 1840
Tongue-and-Groove
Groove (plow)
Tongue
FOR SCRATCHING A SURFACE BEFORE GLUEING
Toothing plane
Compass Plane
OTJ
Carver's Rabbet
only 3" long
the Sun-plane
for levelling barrel-tops

Early American Saws

Both the frame saw and the open saw were in use during the first American settlements. The open saw is very much like its modern counterpart, but it had a handle like that of a knife and it was long enough to be used by two hands. Americans enjoyed using wood in their tools, and the wooden frame saw was most popular. Metal was hard to come by, and the frame saw had the advantage of needing only the narrowest blade.

Saw nomenclature is uncertain, but the most common division is that of "open" and "frame" types. The bow saw (again a frame type) was stretched taut between two arms by a twisted cord (or by rod and screw); the saw blade was readily turned by twisting the handles, making it easy to saw curved pieces.

The buck saw is a bow frame type, but its blade is stationary and heavier, and a long handle has been added. To "buck" logs was to saw them into proper lengths; hence, the buck saw is a woodsman's saw.

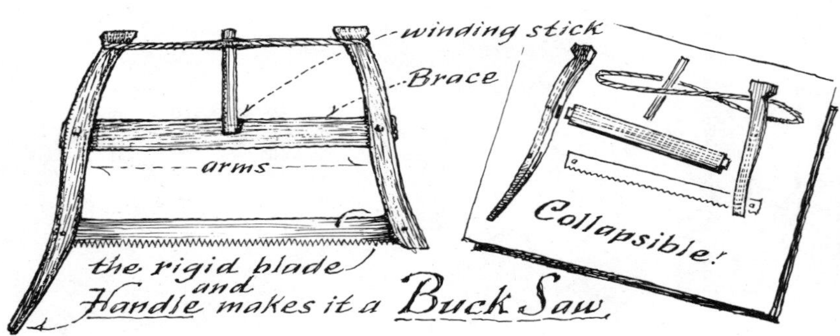

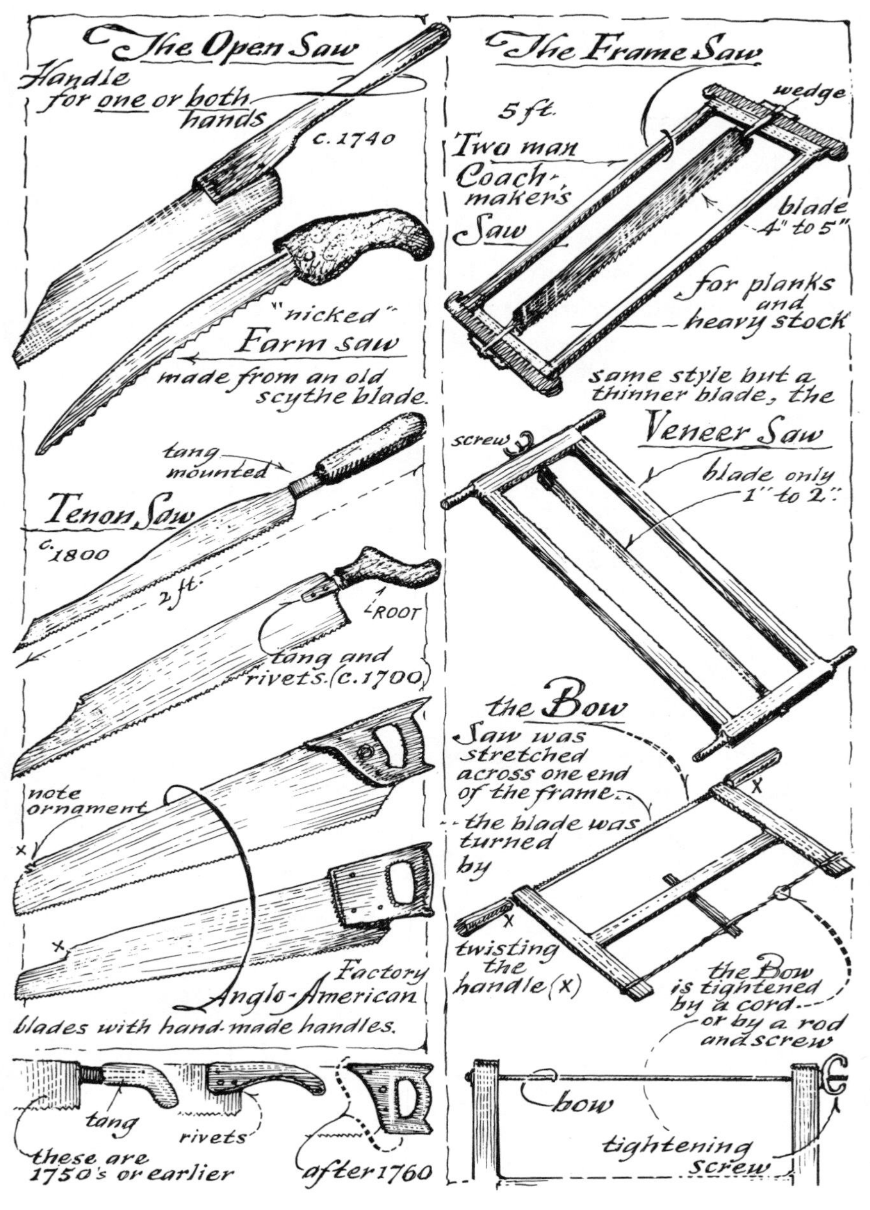
The Open Saw
Handle for one or both hands
c. 1740
"nicked"
Farm saw
made from an old scythe blade.
tang mounted
Tenon Saw
c. 1800
2 ft.
ROOT
tang and rivets (c.1700)
note ornament
Factory
Anglo-American
blades with hand-made handles.
tang
rivets
these are 1750's or earlier
after 1760
The Frame Saw
wedge
5 ft.
Two man Coach-maker's Saw
blade 4" to 5"
for planks and heavy stock
same style but a thinner blade, the
Veneer Saw
screw
blade only 1" to 2"
the Bow
Saw was stretched across one end of the frame..
the blade was turned by
twisting the handle (x)
the Bow is tightened by a cord or by a rod and screw
bow
tightening screw

a Gallery of Frame Saws

The frame saw looks clumsy to us now, but actually it was much more of "an extension of the craftsman's hand" than the modern saw. You can cut straight or around corners with it and always see where the blade was cutting. The modern saw blade is wide, always covering the spot it is cutting, and is restricted to a straight cut.

The terms "chairmaker's saw," "felloe (also "felly") saw," "turning saw," etc. are difficult to pin to one model because each design overlapped the other in size or shape at one time or another. The frame saw is "strained" in the center and two stretchers keep it taut; the bow saw is strained on one end, with a stretcher cord (or rod) on the other.

The finer the work to be done the finer the saw; some frame saws are pieces of art both to work with and to look at.

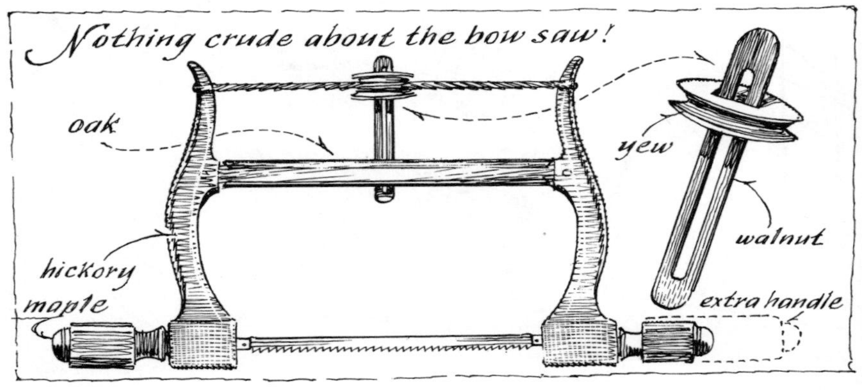

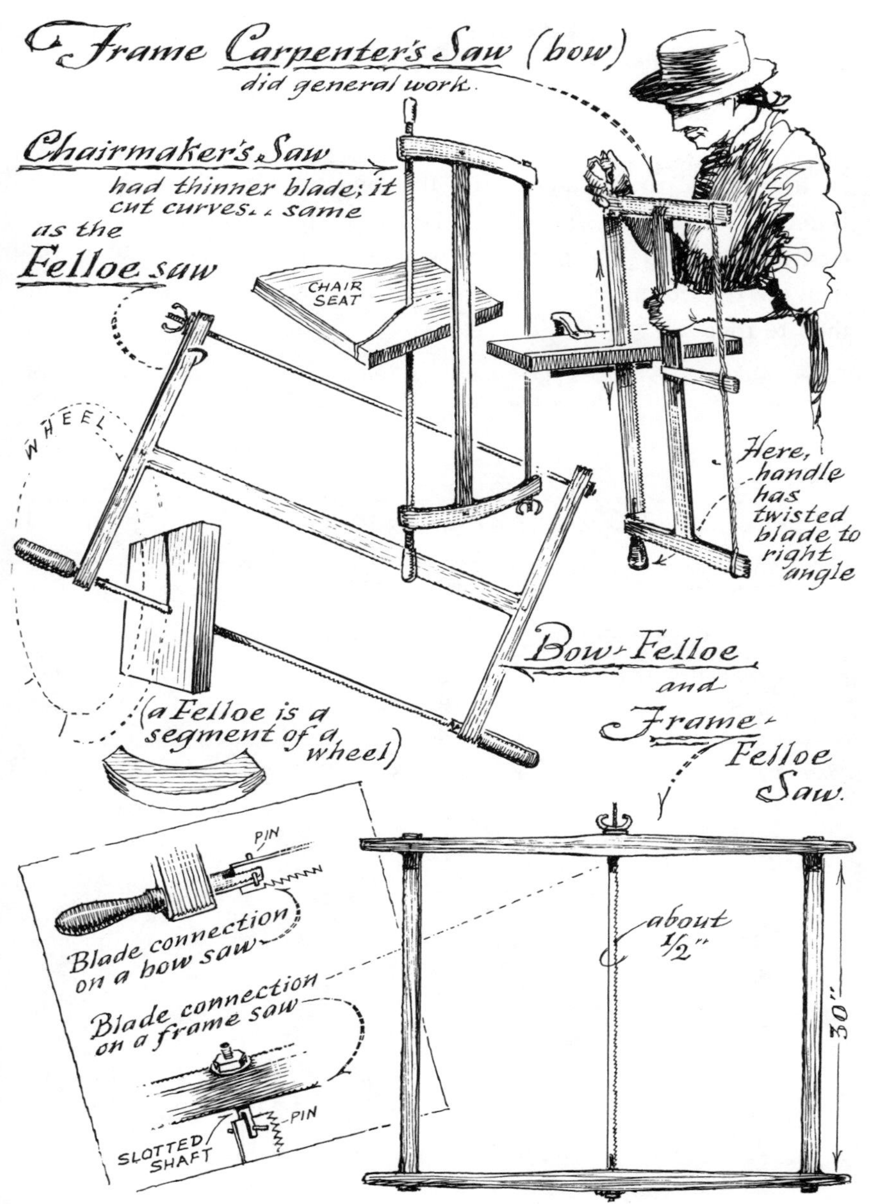
Frame Carpenter's Saw (bow)
did general work.
Chairmaker's Saw
had thinner blade; it cut curves.. same as the
Felloe saw
CHAIR SEAT
WHEEL
Here, handle has twisted blade to right angle
Bow-Felloe
and
Frame-Felloe Saw.
(a Felloe is a segment of a wheel)
PIN
Blade connection on a bow saw
Blade connection on a frame saw
PIN
SLOTTED SHAFT
about 1/2"
30"

The Biggest Saws

Its teeth raked to cut downward, the long pit saws (both open and framed) did most of the earliest American plank-sawing both from trestles and in pits. The open type was more recent in the New World than the framed model. Factory-made, the open pit saw was used until the late 1800's.

There was an ancient open plank saw (see below) that some collectors regard as an open pit saw, but the curved blade and matching handles indicate otherwise.

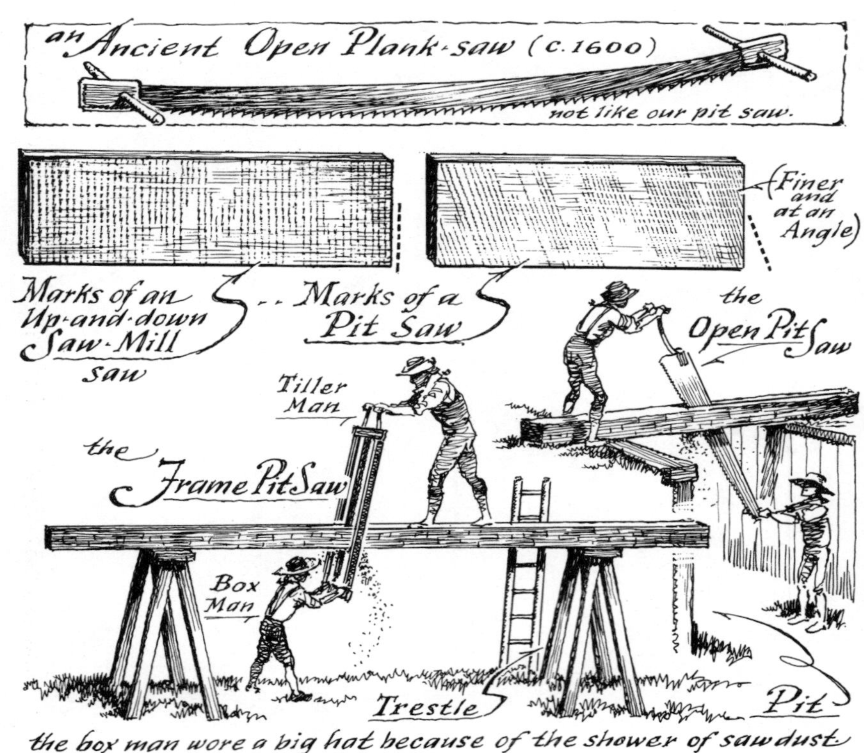

the box man wore a big hat because of the shower of sawdust

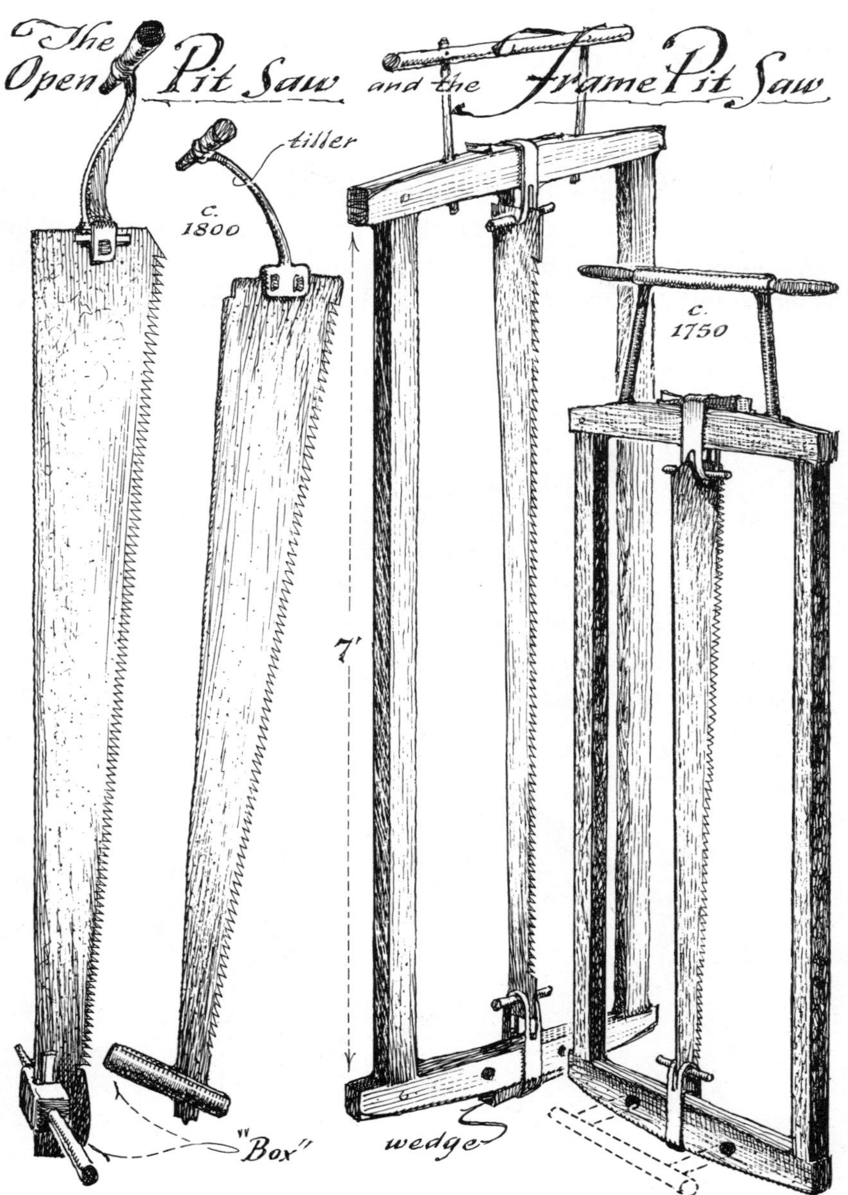
The Open Pit Saw and the Frame Pit Saw
tiller
c. 1800
c. 1750
7'
"Box"
wedge

to Make a Hole

Although awls seem no more than sharp points with handles, there are those who collect them as basic tools. The awl and punch enter wood by "spreading" the fibers apart; the ream, auger, and gimlet "cuts." The "burn auger" (1) was fired to a red-hot point that burned its opening in the wood; then it was twisted to make the hole deeper. The "wood punch" (2) was hammered into the wood, and was twisted both for deeper cut and for release. The "ream awl" (3) had sharp corners that acted as cutting agents.

The "gouge bit" (split-quill) was round-ended, like a gouging chisel; if water was put into its cavity it would run out the end. If water was dropped into a "spoon bit" or "pod auger," it would stay in, for the nose of the bit scoops upward into a twist (A and B). The "twisted cylinder" bit, neither podlike nor triangular, has parallel sides, one of which is a cutting edge. The cutter of the nose auger is shown below, along with the same device on a spiral-ribbon bit.

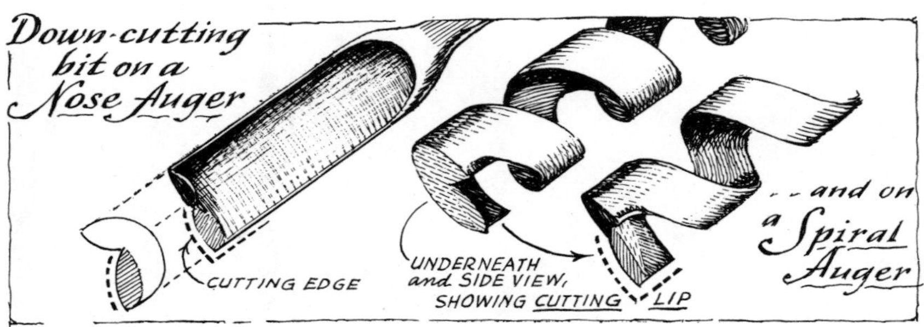

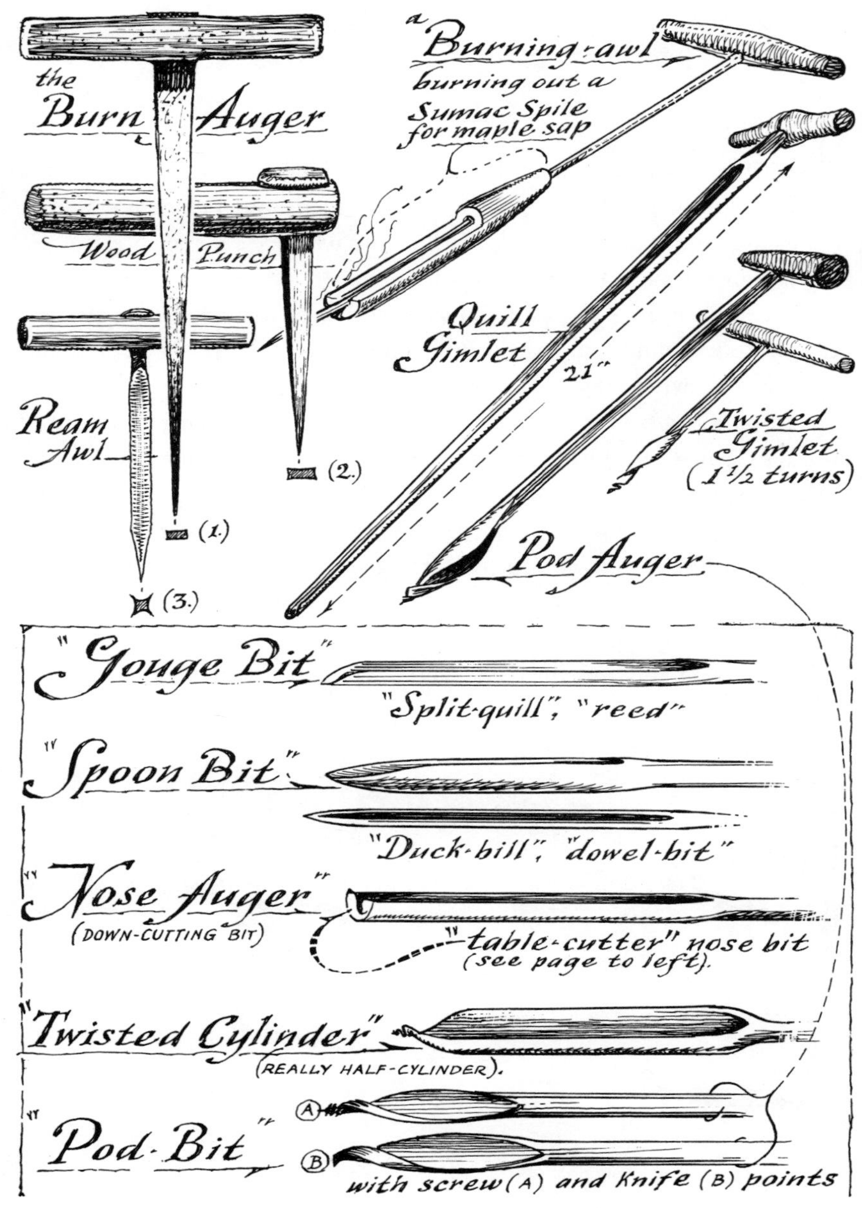
the Burn Auger
a Burning-awl
burning out a Sumac Spile for maple sap
Wood Punch
Quill Gimlet
21"
Ream Awl
(2.)
(1.)
(3.)
Twisted Gimlet (1½ turns)
Pod Auger
"Gouge Bit"
"Split-quill", "reed"
"Spoon Bit"
"Duck-bill", "dowel-bit"
"Nose Auger"
(DOWN-CUTTING BIT)
"table-cutter" nose bit (see page to left).
"Twisted Cylinder"
(REALLY HALF-CYLINDER).
"Pod-Bit"
A
B
with screw (A) and knife (B) points

To Make a Hole Bigger

To enlarge a hole, you may "ream" it with a tapered blade; to be sure, the hole will be tapered too, but often (as when you are cutting a barrel bung-hole or a wheel hub-hole) this is just what you want. The biggest of all reamers is the wheelwright's hub reamer; often it reaches a length of three feet and weighs as much as twenty-five pounds. Some of these can still be found without handles and with strange hooks. Oddly enough, the experts have not decided just how these were used. But I rigged up a wagon wheel on a wheelwright's bench, then put a hooked reamer through the hub, which I had weighted with seventy-five pounds. With two men turning a very long detachable handle (which might explain the missing handles on so many of these blades it worked nicely). With an ordinary reamer, a man exerts about half his weight downward; this can be bettered with a seventy-five-pound weight plus the twenty-five-pound weight of the tool itself.

Tap augers and hub reamers were usually sharpened on one blade (on the inner side).

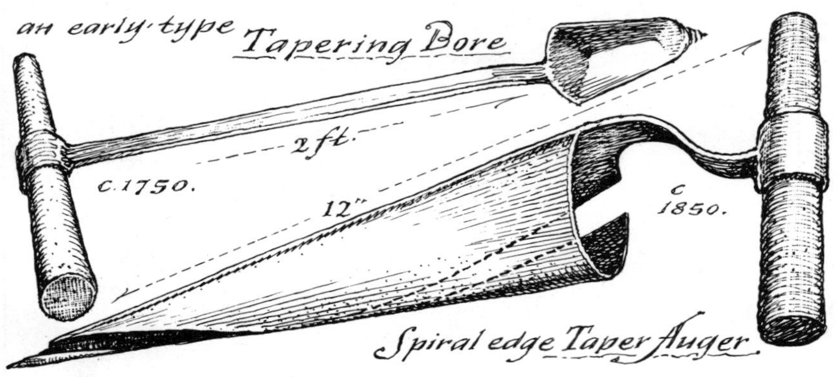

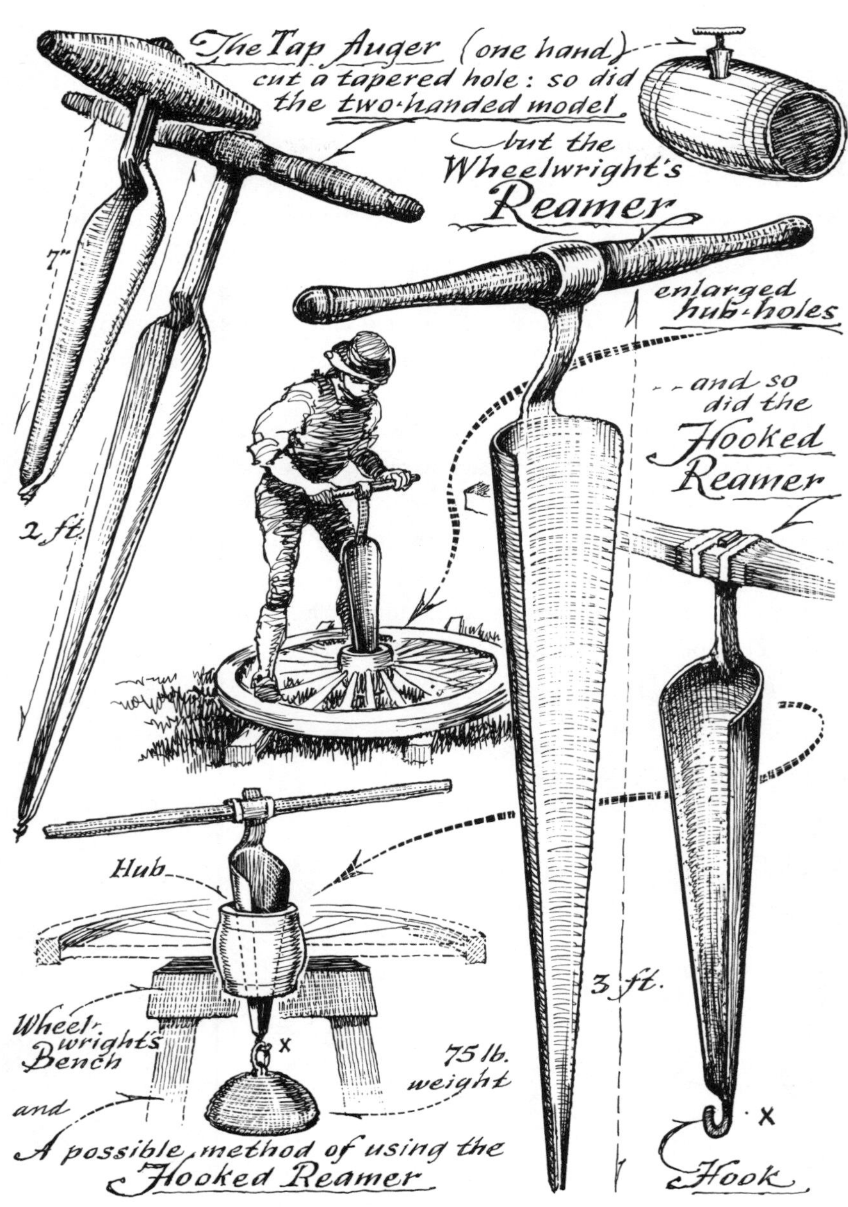
The Tap Auger (one hand)
cut a tapered hole: so did
the two-handed model
but the
Wheelwright's
Reamer
enlarged
hub-holes
--and so
did the
Hooked
Reamer
7"
2 ft.
3 ft.
Hub
Wheel-wright's Bench
and
75 lb.
weight
x
x
A possible method of using the
Hooked Reamer
Hook

to Make a Bigger Hole

Recently a "revolutionary speed bit" was introduced for electric drills. Actually it is an adaptation of an early "button bit" (A) and (B) and has the same design as the "center bit" (c. 1794) with which the pioneer American started trunnel holes in his buildings. For shallow holes or to start a boring, it cut downward without pulling shavings upward as the big spiral bit does. Center bits, therefore, which were never put on bar handles, were used with a brace.

The four typical wooden bar handles shown are generalizations; because so many men made their own handles, it is difficult to pinpoint the date of a handle from its design. I have worked out these estimates, from the handles in my own collection, in the hope that this information might be helpful in dating tools in other collections.

It seems incredible that a man could turn the huge bits that some augers have. The job was made easier in the 1800's by a two-handled drill (shown opposite); an adjustable model came out in the 1860's that drilled at any angle.

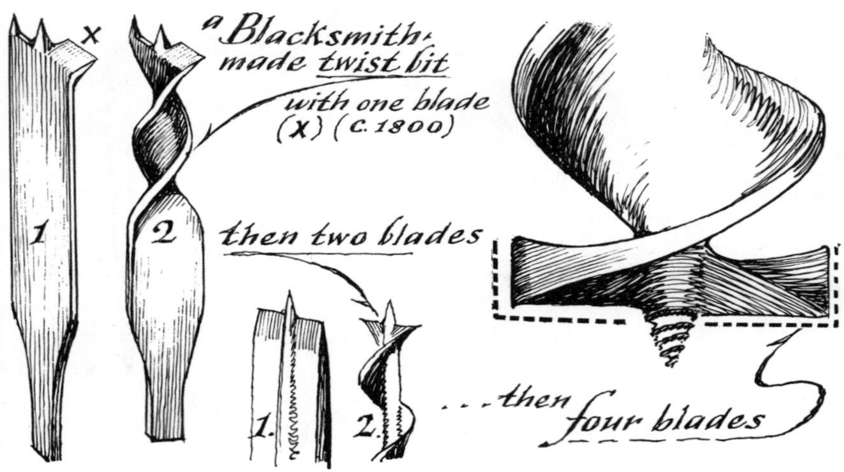

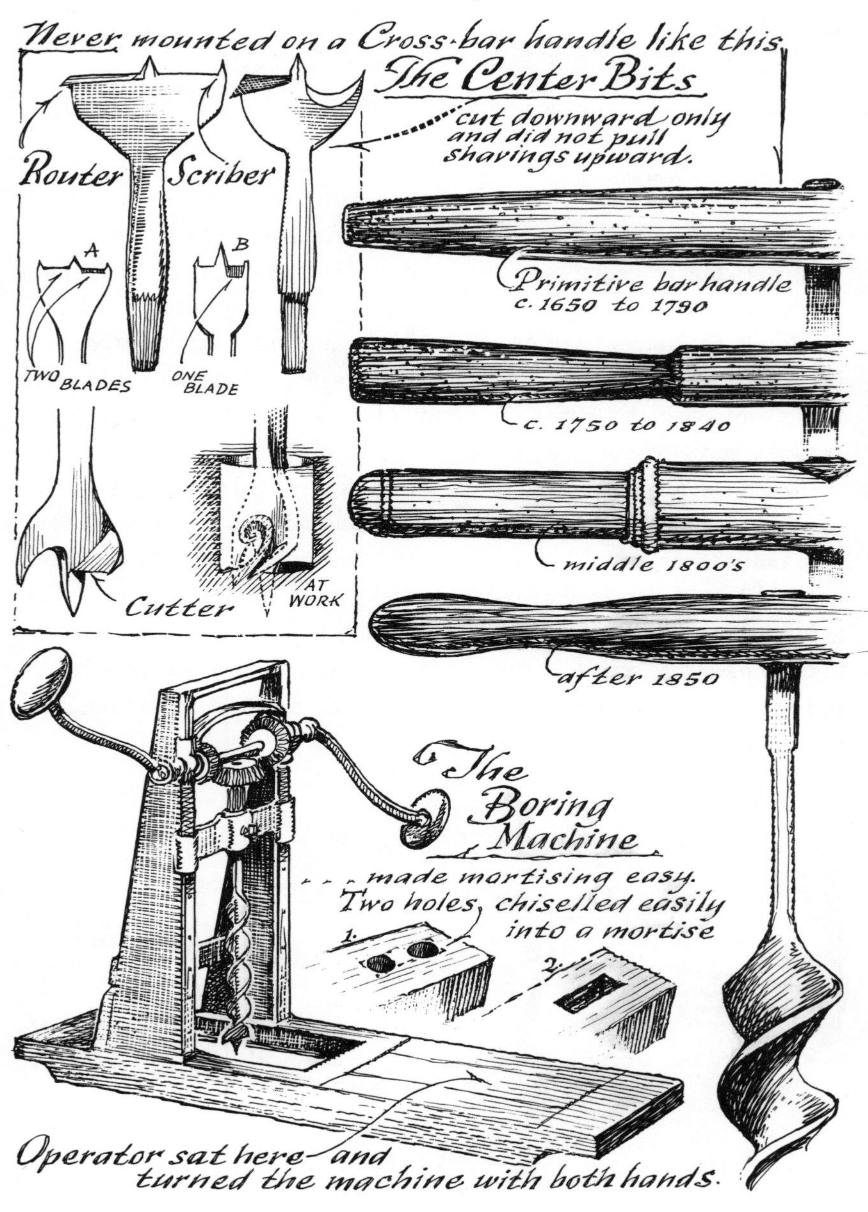
Never mounted on a Cross-bar handle like this
The Center Bits
cut downward only
and did not pull
shavings upward.
Router
Scriber
A
B
TWO BLADES
ONE BLADE
Cutter
AT
WORK
Primitive bar handle
c. 1650 to 1790
c. 1750 to 1840
middle 1800's
after 1850
The Boring Machine
... made mortising easy.
Two holes, chiselled easily
into a mortise
1.
2.
Operator sat here—and
turned the machine with both hands.

The Brace or Bitstock

The early American bitstock or brace was made of native seasoned hardwood. Some of the earliest were made of natural-shaped roots or boughs (see drawing in center, opposite page). Oak and hickory were most commonly used although the burl-wood bitstock was also prized.

Most early braces (particularly in New England) were "bitted" in a permanent manner; the bit was moulded into a metal wad and fitted tightly into a square wooden chuck (sometimes ferruled), and this square chuck was wedged into the stock to stay.

The revolving buttons were masterpieces of woodworking, for most of those on the earliest braces still work nicely and are not even cracked. The button was either "stayed" by a wooden pin through the shaft and head (A), or the shaft was "stayed" by a "Cotter-pinlike" peg (B). The natural-shape stock's button was loose, staying in just by pressure. (As some braces were rested against the chest—and therefore needed a bigger and flatter button—this brace may have had interchangeable buttons, one for the hand and one for the chest.)

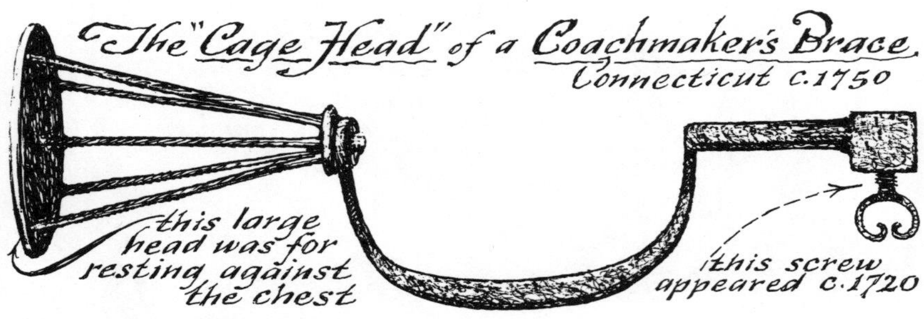
The "Cage Head" of a Coachmaker's Brace
Connecticut c.1750
this large head was for resting against the chest
this screw appeared c.1720

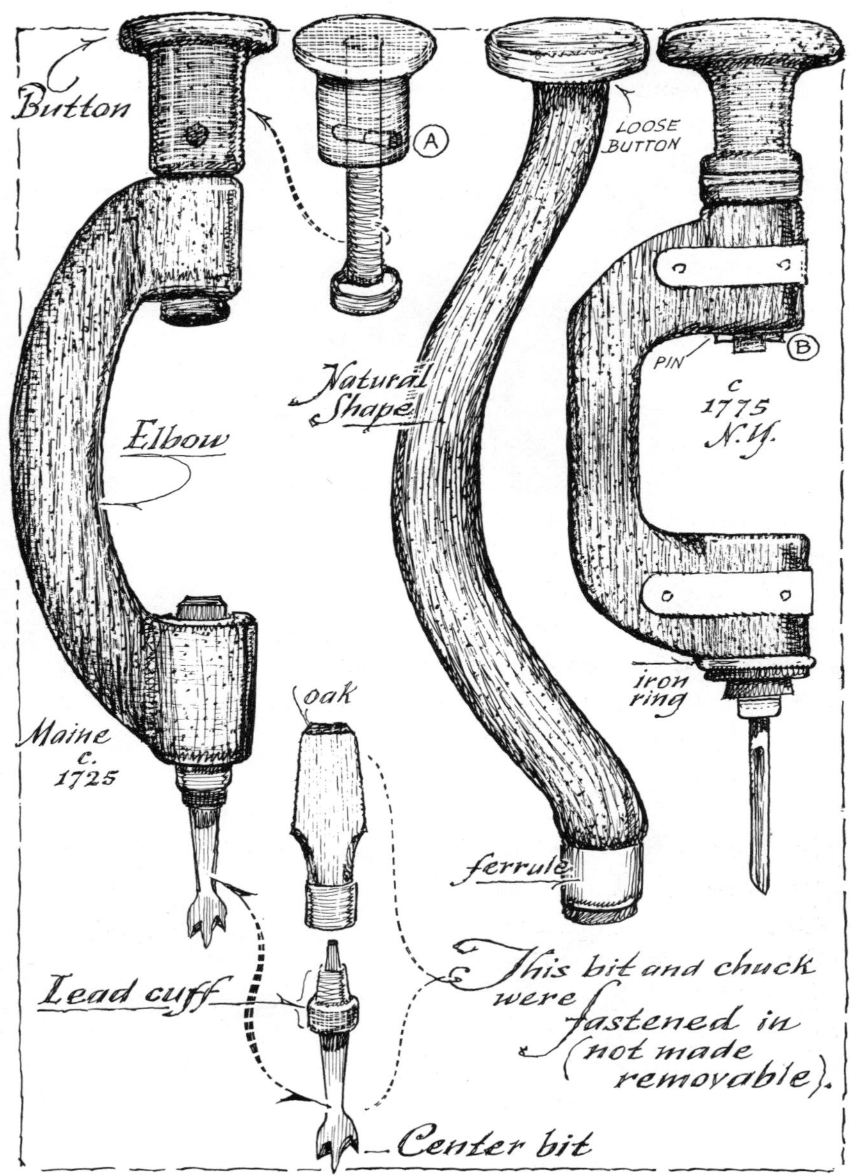
Button
A
LOOSE BUTTON
Natural Shape
PIN
B
c 1775 N.Y.
Elbow
oak
iron ring
Maine c. 1725
ferrule
This bit and chuck were fastened in (not made removable).
Lead cuff
Center bit

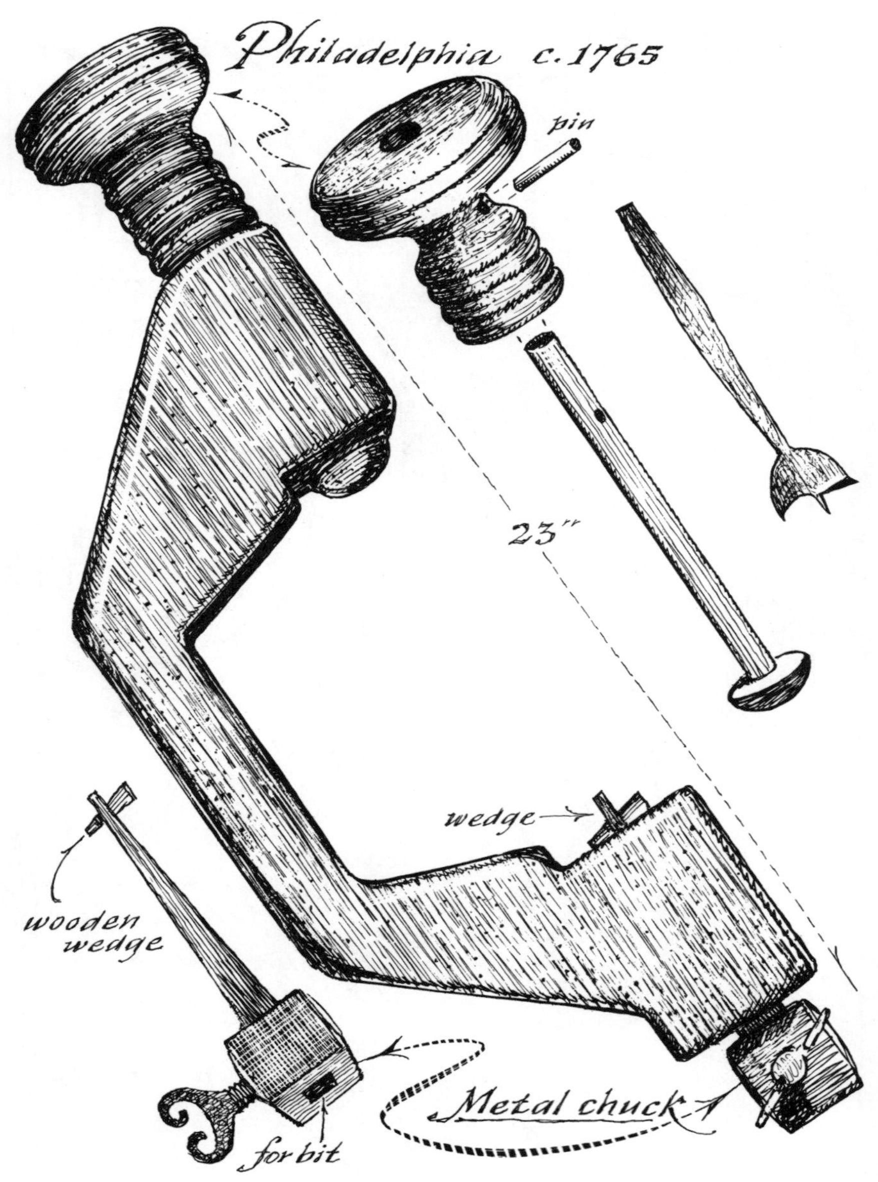
Philadelphia c.1765
pin
23"
wedge
wooden
wedge
for bit
Metal chuck

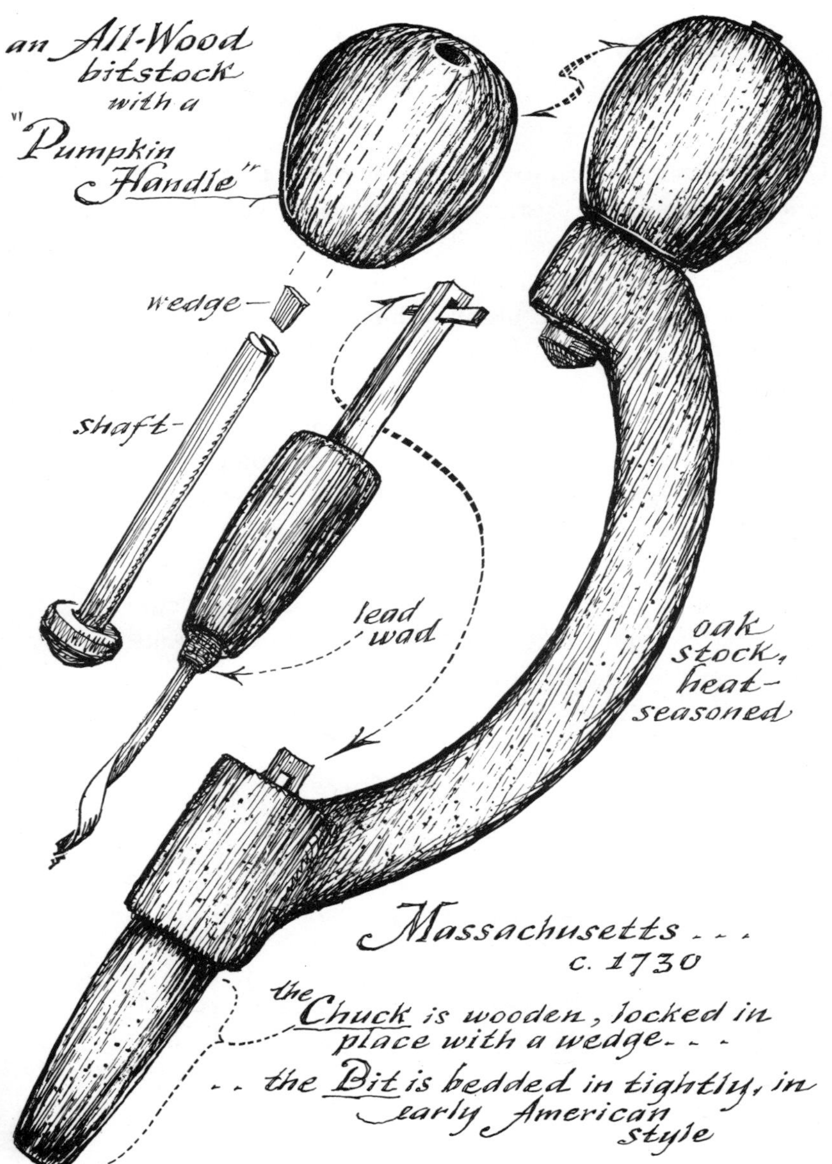
an All-Wood
bitstock
with a
"Pumpkin
Handle"
wedge-
shaft-
lead
wad
oak
stock,
heat-
seasoned
Massachusetts . . .
c. 1730
the Chuck is wooden, locked in
place with a wedge . . .
. . the Bit is bedded in tightly, in
early American
style

The THINGS you'll find in a Barn!

One of the most popular pages of the monthly publication of a tool collectors' club is its "Whatsis Column." Antique gadgets that stump the experts are frequently turning up. In the era of hand-made tools, it was logical that one-of-a-kind implements were created—the man who custom-made his own tools could allow himself the luxury of making tools to meet *his* needs. Then, too, there were devices that had many uses. Ladders were used as tobacco driers; the bars of a ladder-back chair held candleholders; meat hooks doubled as grappling hooks that retrieved things from the bottoms of wells. If you think it strange that a hook was so necessary to a household, remember that the well was used many times a day, that foods needing refrigeration were often lowered into it. Items lost beneath the water could not, of course, be seen, so they could be retrieved only by groping. The well hook was used as much as any other implement of the old-time household. After all, who wanted to drink water from a well filled with old pails?

These tiny Hammers were not Carpenters'.. they were hung on sleds.. ..They knocked snow from horses' hoofs.
all iron
5½"
called Yankee Snow Knockers

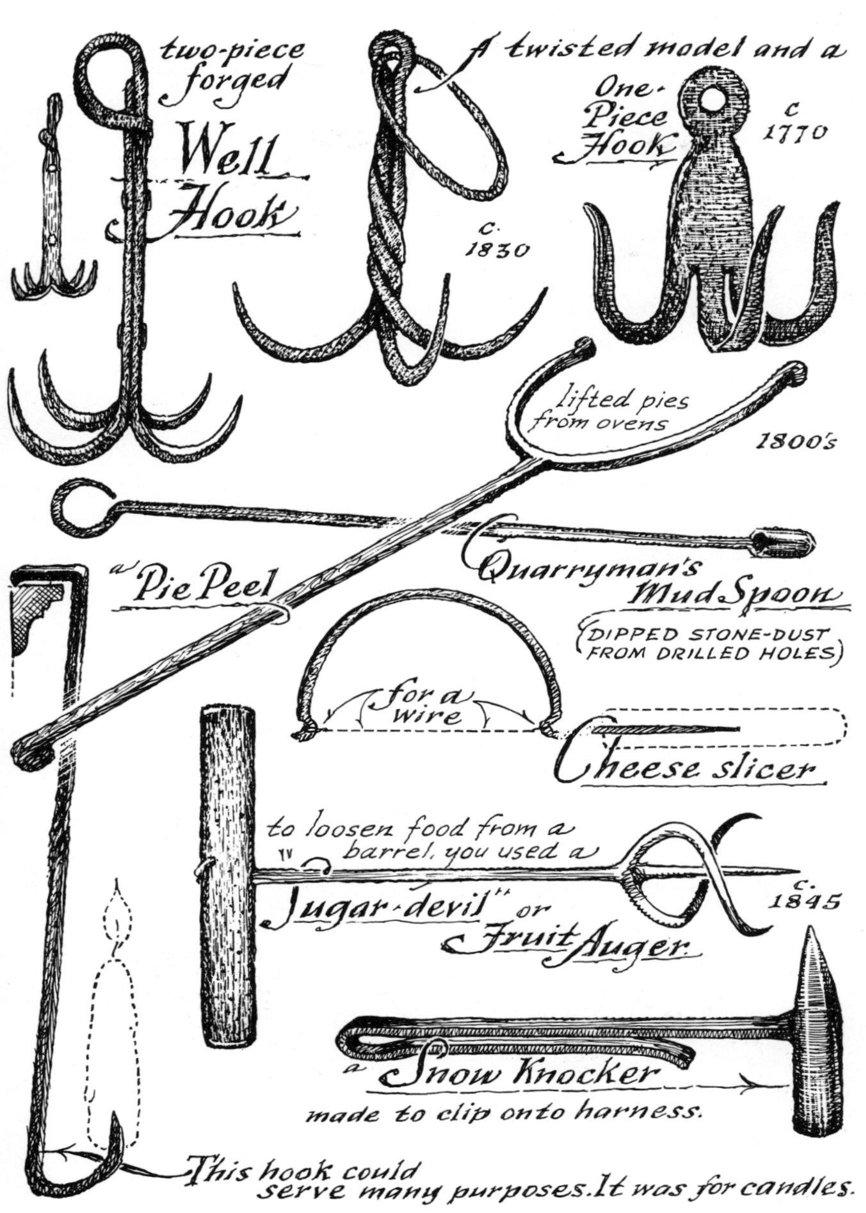
two-piece forged
Well Hook
A twisted model and a
One-Piece Hook
c 1770
c. 1830
lifted pies from ovens
1800's
a Pie Peel
Quarryman's Mud Spoon
(DIPPED STONE-DUST FROM DRILLED HOLES)
for a wire
Cheese slicer
to loosen food from a barrel, you used a
"Sugar-devil" or
Fruit Auger
c. 1845
a Snow Knocker
made to clip onto harness.
This hook could serve many purposes. It was for candles.

Some were Special

Although nails and hooks and tacks and hundreds of other iron implements were hammered out by farmers all over the countryside, it was recognized as fitting that each item have its own sizes and patterns. The nails made in Maine look quite like the nails made in New Jersey, both in proportions and design; only an expert can tell a difference. People were religious about conforming to tradition; they had a profound reverence for accepted design that we nowadays feel is decadence.

Here are a few things that are of the past that you might find in old attics or barns, each thing for a special use. The stock-knife shaped wood, the mill pick dressed millstones, the barrel-scrape cleaned out barrels, the "commander" pushed beams "home" and into their mortises.

When I was trying to move a barn, I found a "commander" of better use than two men working with sledgehammers, and was pleased to see it sending beams into place without disfiguring them as the iron sledges did.

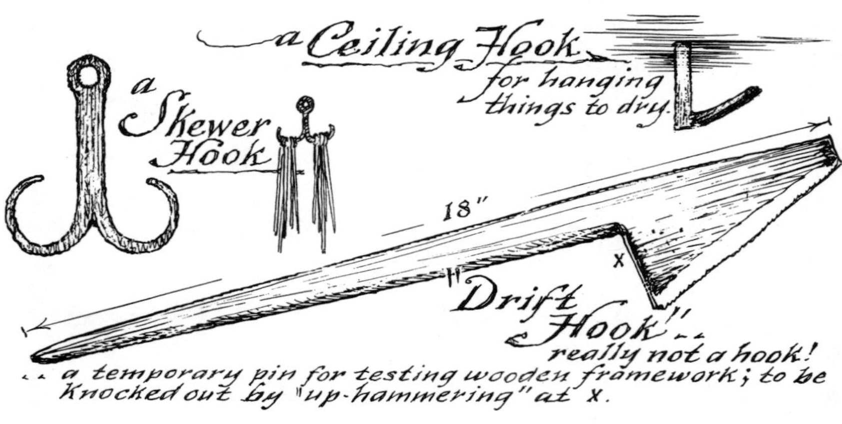
a Ceiling Hook
for hanging things to dry.
a Skewer Hook
18"
x
"Drift Hook"..
really not a hook!
.. a temporary pin for testing wooden framework; to be Knocked out by "up-hammering" at x.

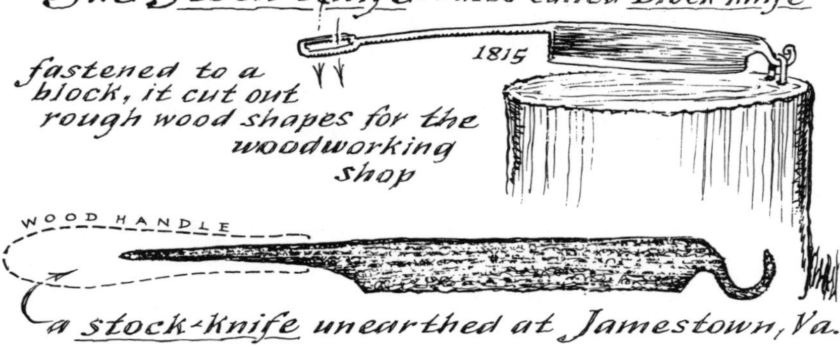
The Stock-Knife .. also called Block-Knife
1815
fastened to a block, it cut out rough wood shapes for the woodworking shop
WOOD HANDLE
a stock-knife unearthed at Jamestown, Va.

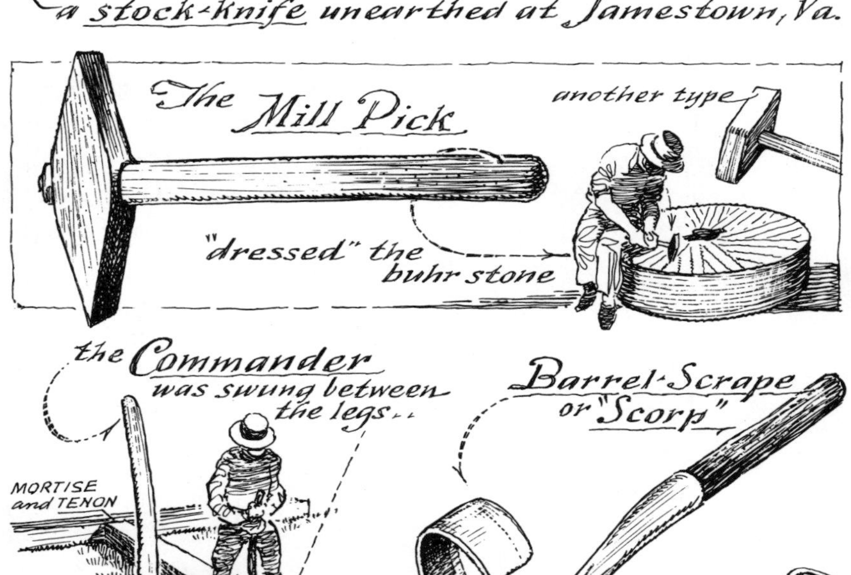
The Mill Pick
another type
"dressed" the buhr stone
the Commander was swung between the legs..
MORTISE and TENON
to pound beams "home." before raising.

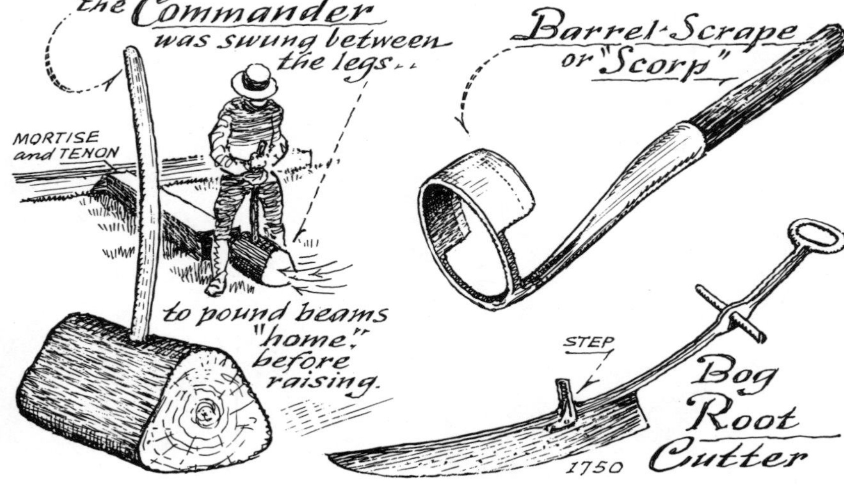
Barrel-Scrape or "Scorp"
STEP
Bog Root Cutter
1750

These were Tools too!

"Sleds" were for winter; "sledges" were used year round. Tools the sledges were. If you would wish to learn the value of the sledge, try putting an ordinary house broom beneath a heavy trunk or object you wish to move. With someone then lifting one end, a child can easily pull the broom and its load across the floor. Farmers pulled unbelievable loads (on wooden runners) across grass on which a wheel would have sunk and become impossible. We know of the "stone boat," but the Early American farmer had a number of other sledge-type devices before the wheelbarrow. A sledge could be pulled by horse or ox through forest, and over rocks and onto the farm in winter ice or spring mud, whereas a wheeled vehicle could not. A wheeled vehicle is higher off the ground; this makes it inconveniently high for lifting loads *into* and it does tip over easily. So, harvesting and haying and moving rocks, dung, maple syrup barrels, etc. was done by sledge rather than wagon.

Here you may see a few of these early sliding devices. It might be safely said that for every wagon on the Early American farm, there were three to ten sledges. Even the hand-pulled model, like that shown below, was used until the early 1800's.

Even after horse and wagon vehicles,
the Tumbril Sledge remained
as a handy farm tool.
1650

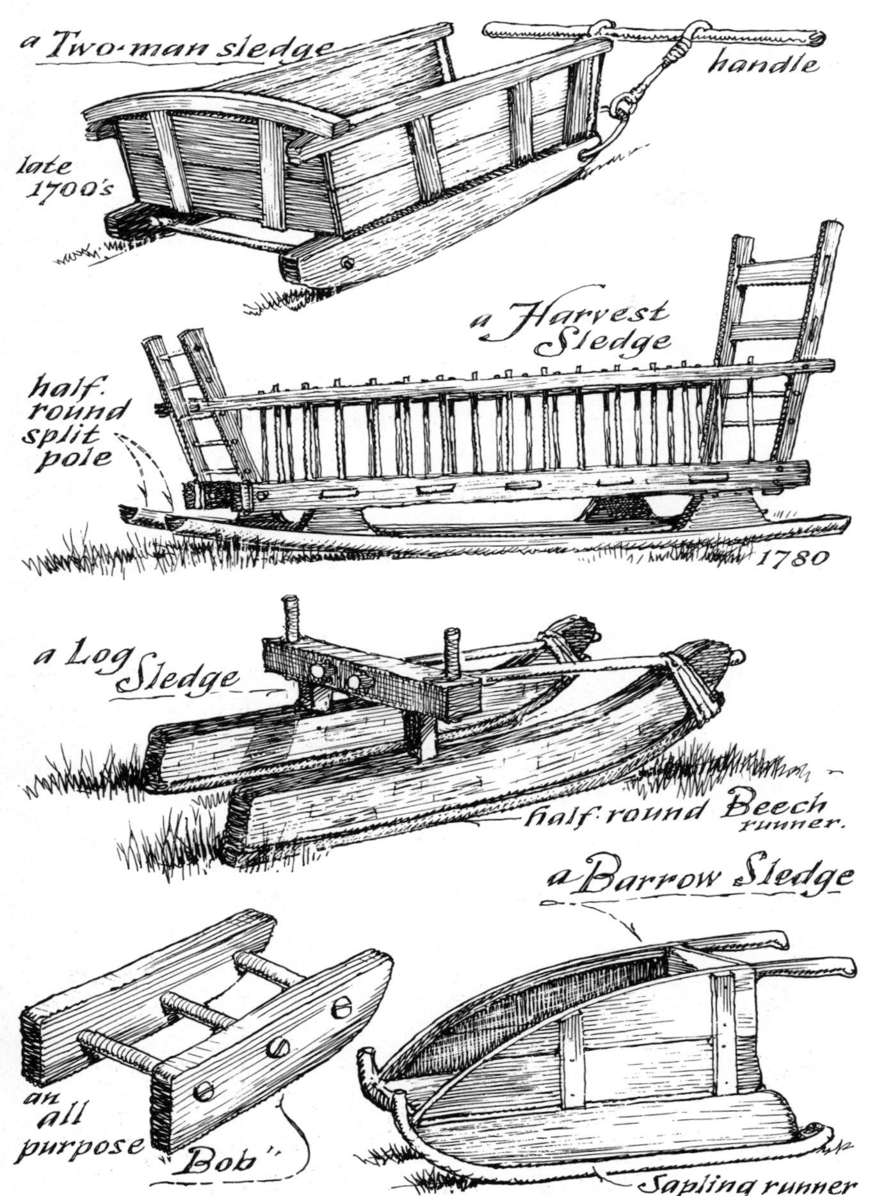
a Two-man sledge
handle
late 1700's
a Harvest Sledge
half-round split pole
1780
a Log Sledge
half-round Beech runner.
a Barrow Sledge
an all purpose "Bob"
Sapling runner

Jacks

The Early American was an artist at lifting and moving heavy objects. Foundations and stone fences were built with the lever principle and a few gadgets as well as with the help of oxen. Experts are often stumped by the strange hooks and loops of iron with teeth in them that are found in old barns. But these were blacksmith-made jack hooks for moving beams and logs and stones. The lever was any handy tree limb; the longer, the more leverage.

The "wagon jacks" you find in antique shops were used for many purposes. Carpenters, framers, blacksmiths, and wheelwrights included these jacks in their list of shop tools. Some of them are made entirely of wood (usually ash or hickory); and they have outlasted many automobile jacks that have rusted away and ended in the junk pile while the wooden jacks are as good as they were a century ago.

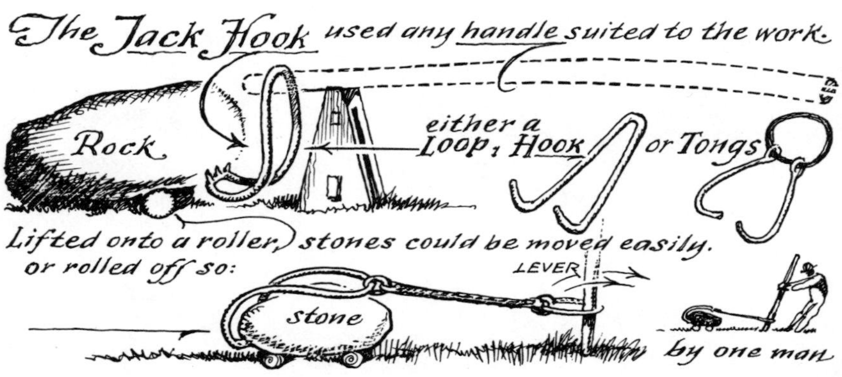
The Jack Hook used any handle suited to the work.
Rock
either a
Loop, Hook or Tongs
Lifted onto a roller, stones could be moved easily.
or rolled off so:
LEVER
stone
by one man

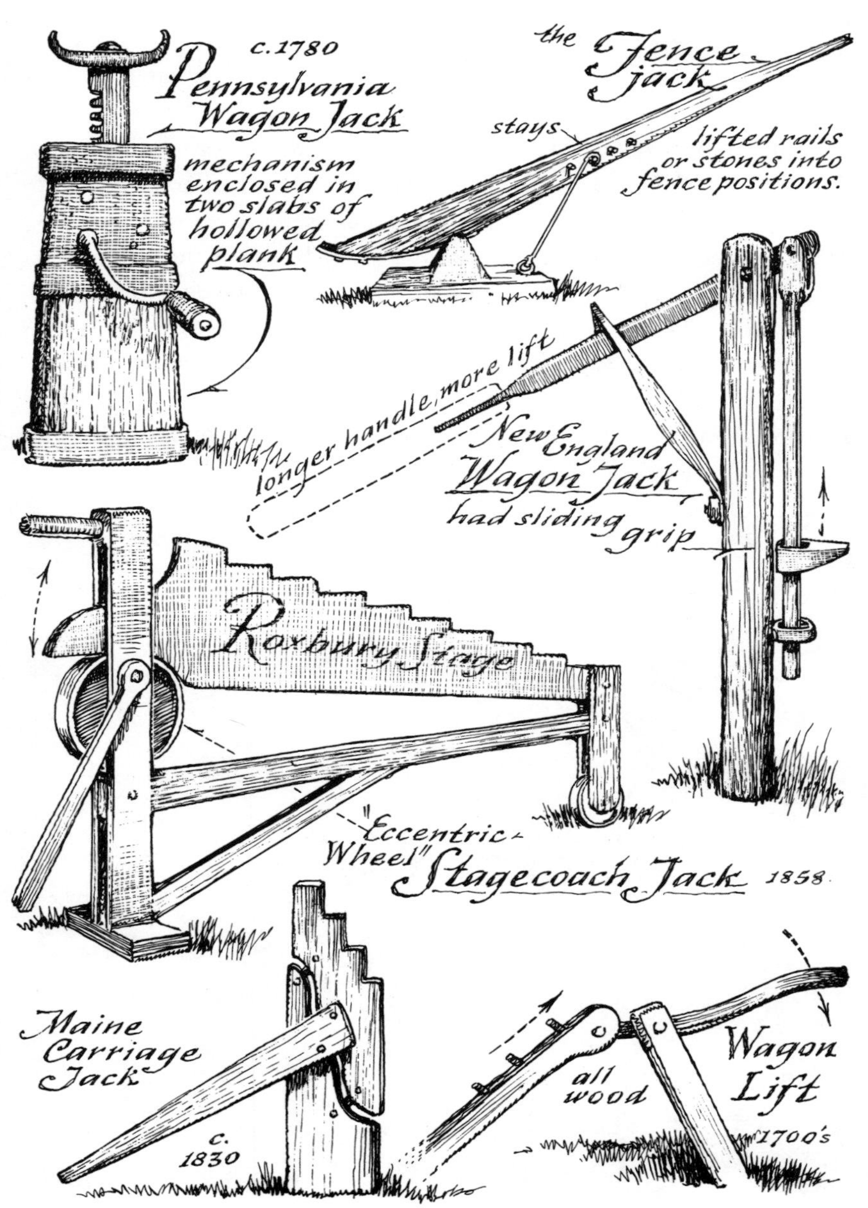
c.1780
Pennsylvania Wagon Jack
mechanism enclosed in two slabs of hollowed plank
the Fence jack
stays
lifted rails or stones into fence positions.
longer handle, more lift
New England Wagon Jack
had sliding grip
Roxbury Stage
"Eccentric Wheel" Stagecoach Jack 1858
Maine Carriage Jack
c. 1830
all wood
Wagon Lift
1700's

The Blacksmith

"Smith" from "smite," "black" from "black metal" (as distinguished from silversmith brightwork), the "blacksmith" was the Early American handyman. He made nails, hinges, sled runners, anchors, scythes, hoes, utensils, axes, hooks, and every kind of tool. In the middle 1800's he began taking over the farrier's work of horseshoeing; till then the farrier was veterinary too.

Blacksmith tool design has not changed very much except for the hazelwood withes that held all upper tools (chisels and swages). Hardly an implement or utensil cannot be traced to the early blacksmith.

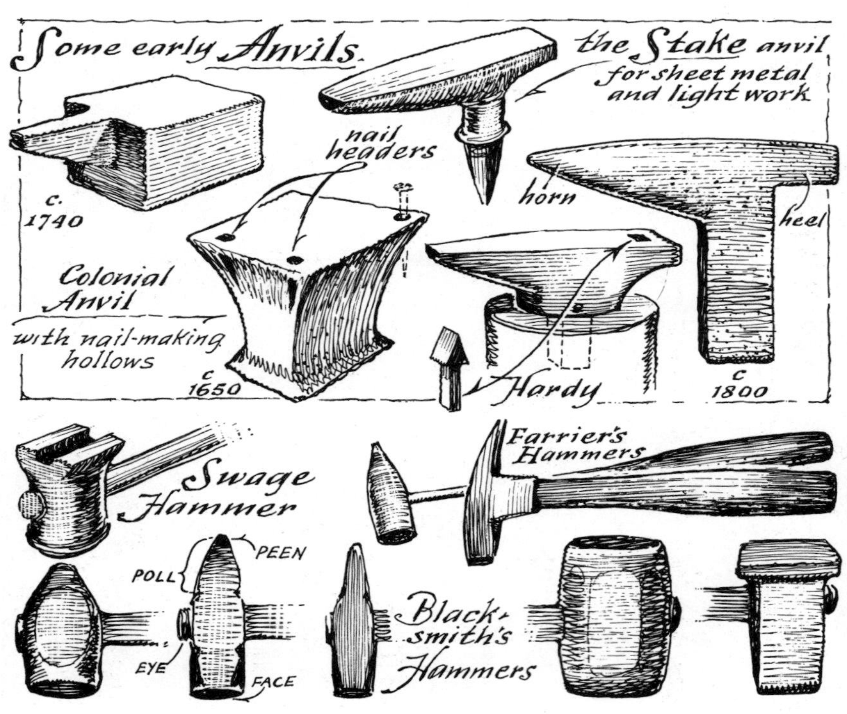

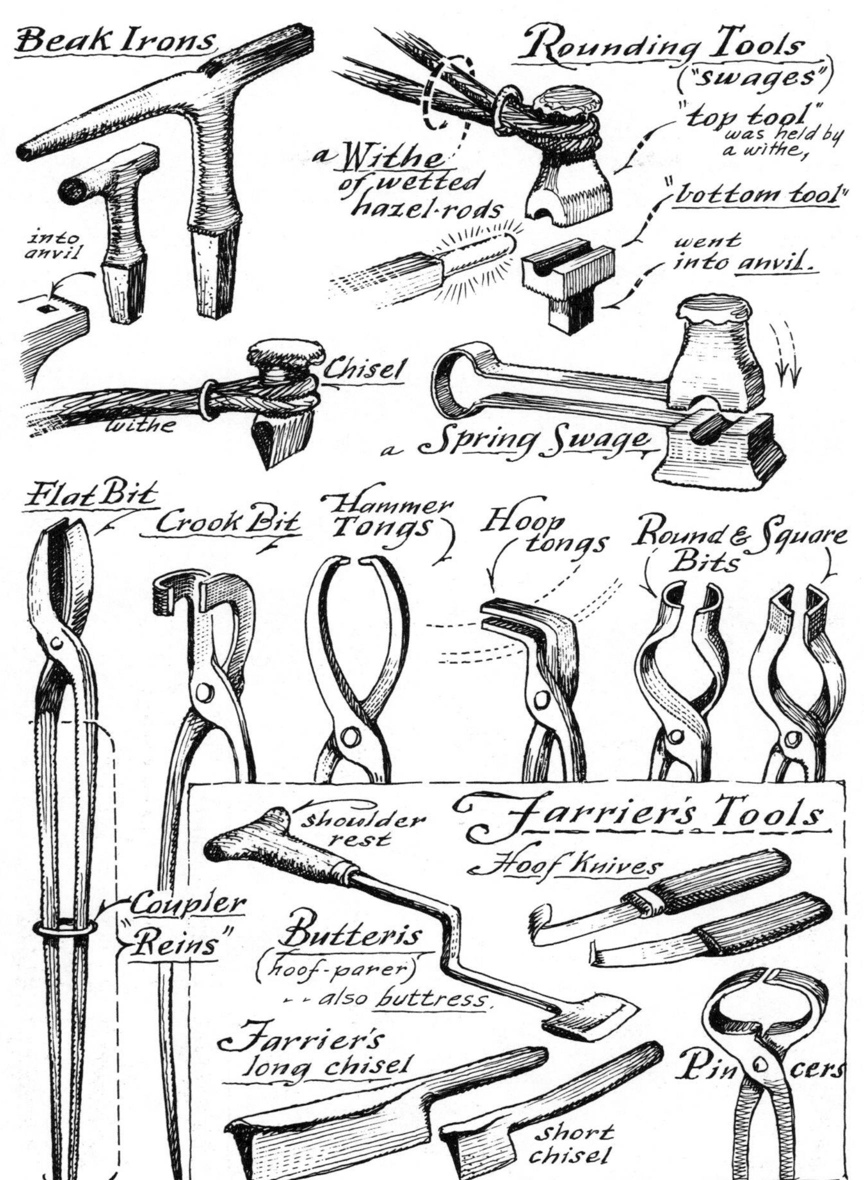
Beak Irons
into anvil
Rounding Tools
("swages")
"top tool" was held by a withe,
a Withe of wetted hazel-rods
"bottom tool"
went into anvil.
Chisel
withe
a Spring Swage
Flat Bit
Crook Bit
Hammer Tongs
Hoop tongs
Round & Square Bits
Coupler
"Reins"
Farrier's Tools
shoulder rest
Hoof Knives
Butteris
(hoof-parer)
-- also buttress.
Farrier's long chisel
Pincers
short chisel

Wrought Nailmaking

Lacking in beauty, the "nail header" is hardly a collector's prize, yet its plainness does not adequately explain its infrequent appearance in antique shops. Considering how farmers made nails by the thousands during winter months around the forge or fireplace, the rarity of headers is a mystery.

Machine-cut nails taper only on two sides; wrought nails on four. The most common "rose nail" had four hammer hits (if done by an expert); the head of the "clasp nail" had sharp downward sides to cut into the surface; "plancher nails" had T-shaped heads to hold down flooring; the "scupper" nailed leather (as for a bellows). Though our "brad" is a small-headed nail, the word once meant "broad" and the "brad" was such a nail for planks.

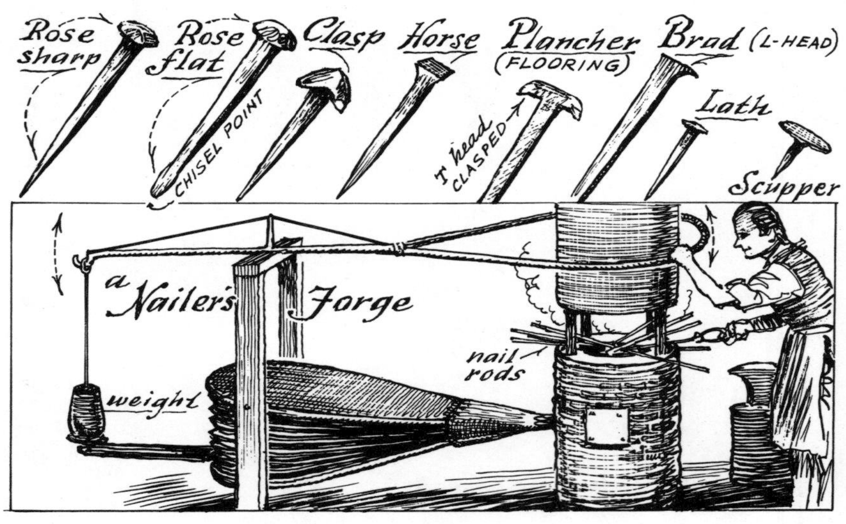

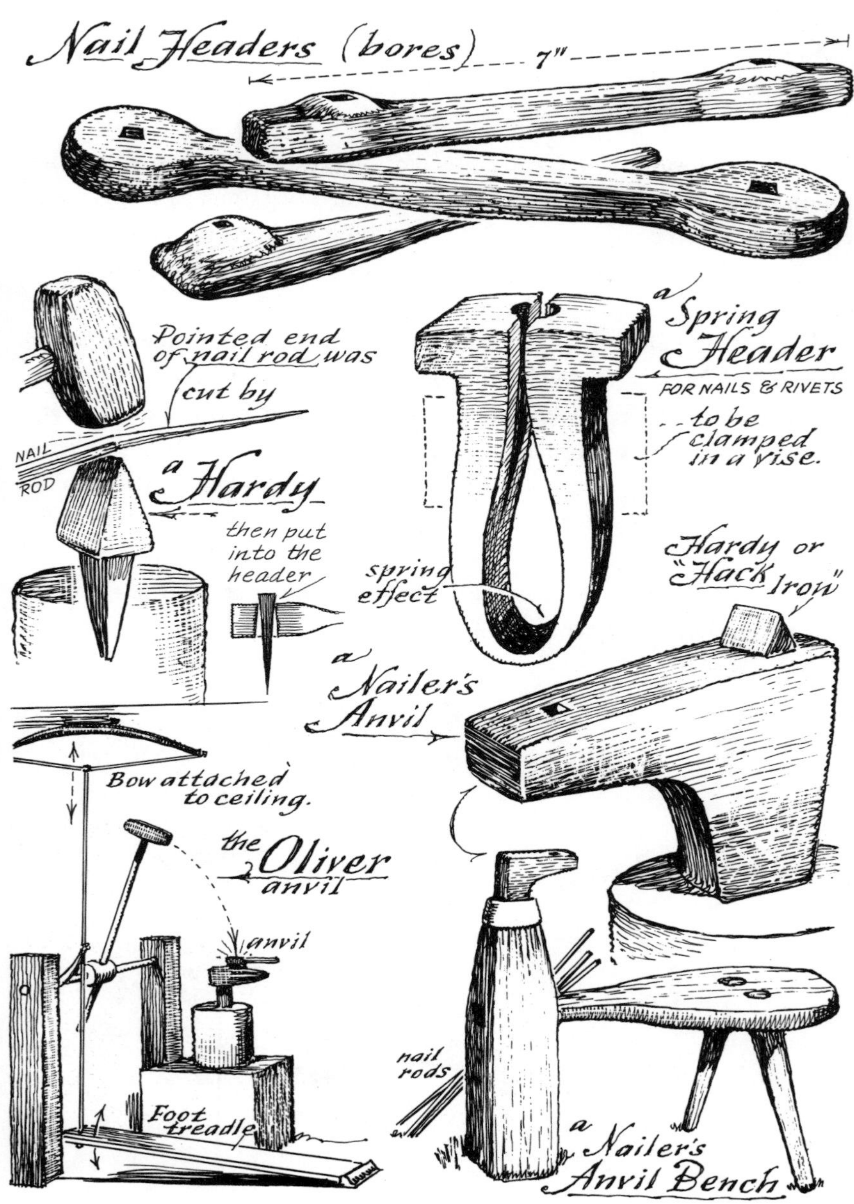
Nail Headers (bores)
7"
Pointed end of nail rod was cut by
NAIL ROD
a Hardy
then put into the header
a Spring Header
FOR NAILS & RIVETS
to be clamped in a vise.
spring effect
Hardy or "Hack Iron"
a Nailer's Anvil
Bow attached to ceiling.
the Oliver anvil
anvil
Foot treadle
nail rods
a Nailer's Anvil Bench

Tanners and Curriers

A currier did *not* curry horses. His craft was to scrape and soften the rough hides after the tanner had treated them. The tanner's tools, so wet and messy when being used, were seldom things of beauty, but their lines were traditional and graceful. The tanner's knives had delicate curves to fit the curve of the tanner's beam.

The currier's beam was flat, just as his knife was. The shaving knife (also called beamer or head-knife) had a soft steel blade with its fine edge burred over (recurved) into a minute scraper form. This delicate edge needed constant turning with a "turning steel" and lifting with a "finger steel," which was kept handy between two fingers as the beamsman worked. (This recurved edge will have disappeared from wear and corrosion on ancient tools.)

Farmers made their own leather for shoes, hinges, and harness, so old barns often have such tools about.

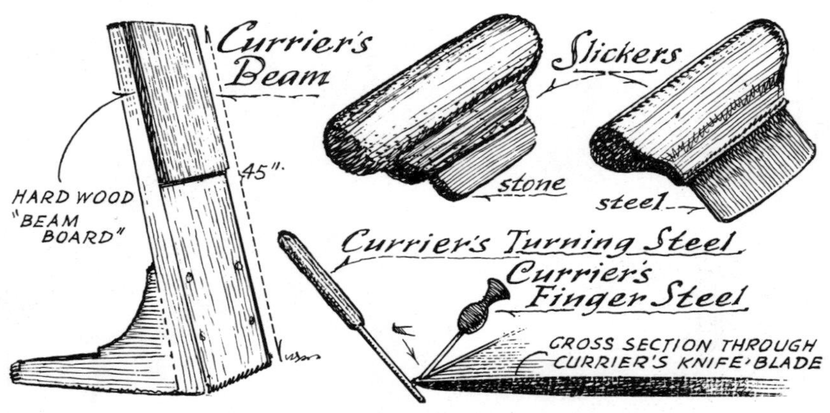

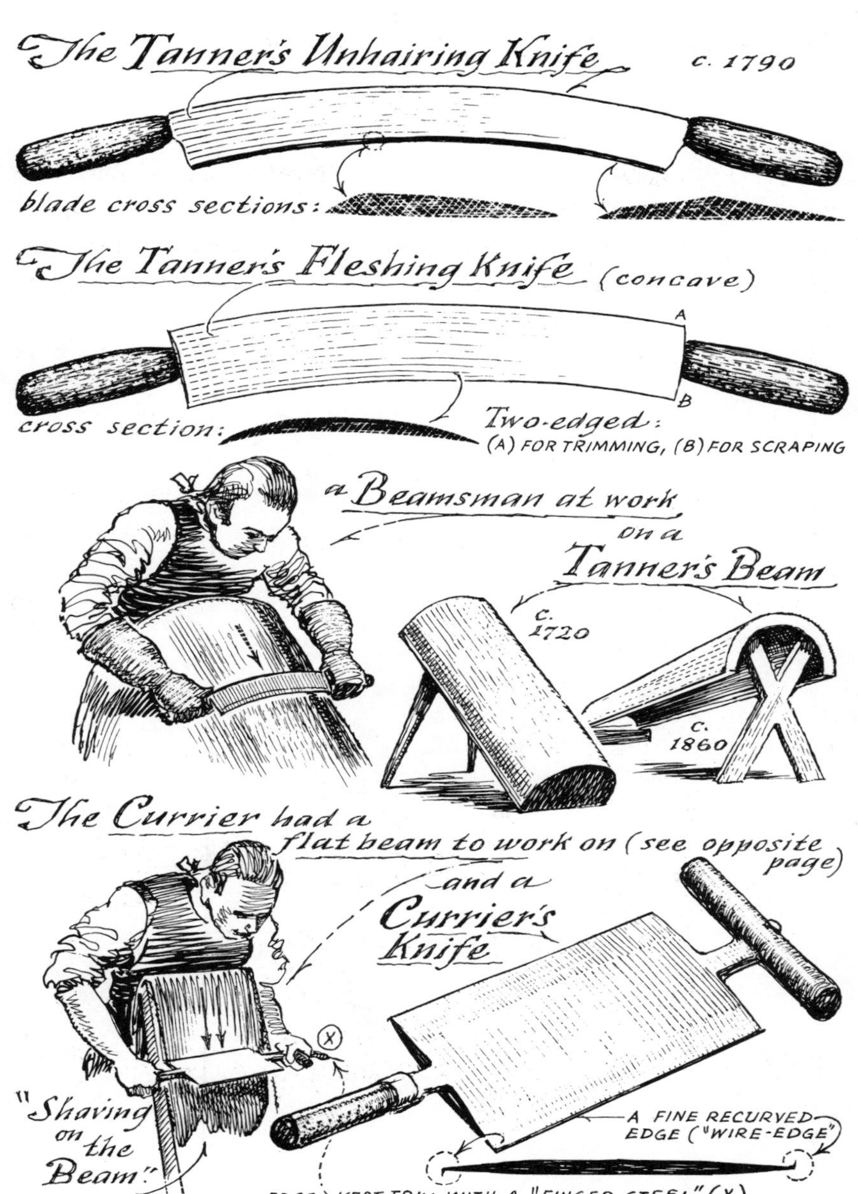
The Tanner's Unhairing Knife c. 1790
blade cross sections:
The Tanner's Fleshing Knife (concave)
A
B
cross section:
Two-edged:
(A) FOR TRIMMING, (B) FOR SCRAPING
a Beamsman at work
on a
Tanner's Beam
c. 1720
c. 1860
The Currier had a
flat beam to work on (see opposite page)
and a
Currier's Knife
(X)
"Shaving on the Beam."
A FINE RECURVED EDGE ("WIRE-EDGE")
EDGE KEPT TRIM WITH A "FINGER STEEL" (X)

About Wheels

Early wheelwright tools were not much different from those of hardwood joinery except for those shown here. The process of putting a wheel together is illustrated below. The tire (iron outer rim) was made by the blacksmith. After the tire was made hot in a bed of ashes, it was applied to the wooden wheel, and then cooled quickly. The contraction tightened the tire, and held the whole wheel together with a tremendous force.

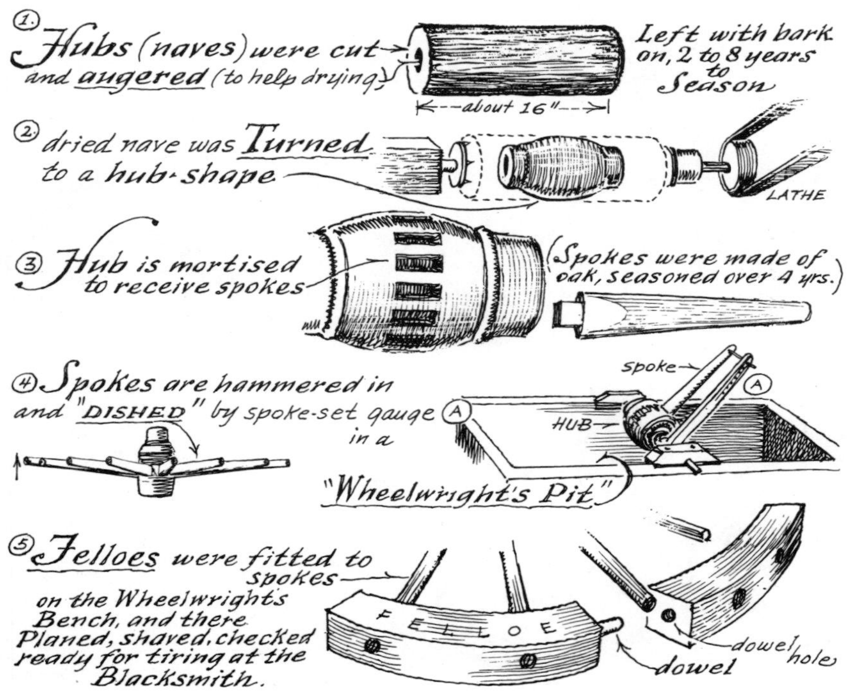

1. Hubs (naves) were cut and augered (to help drying)
Left with bark on, 2 to 8 years to Season
about 16"
2. dried nave was Turned to a hub-shape
LATHE
3. Hub is mortised to receive spokes
(Spokes were made of oak, seasoned over 4 yrs.)
4. Spokes are hammered in and "DISHED" by spoke-set gauge (A) in a "Wheelwright's Pit"
spoke
(A)
HUB
5. Felloes were fitted to spokes on the Wheelwright's Bench, and there Planed, shaved, checked ready for tiring at the Blacksmith.
FELLOE
dowel
dowel hole

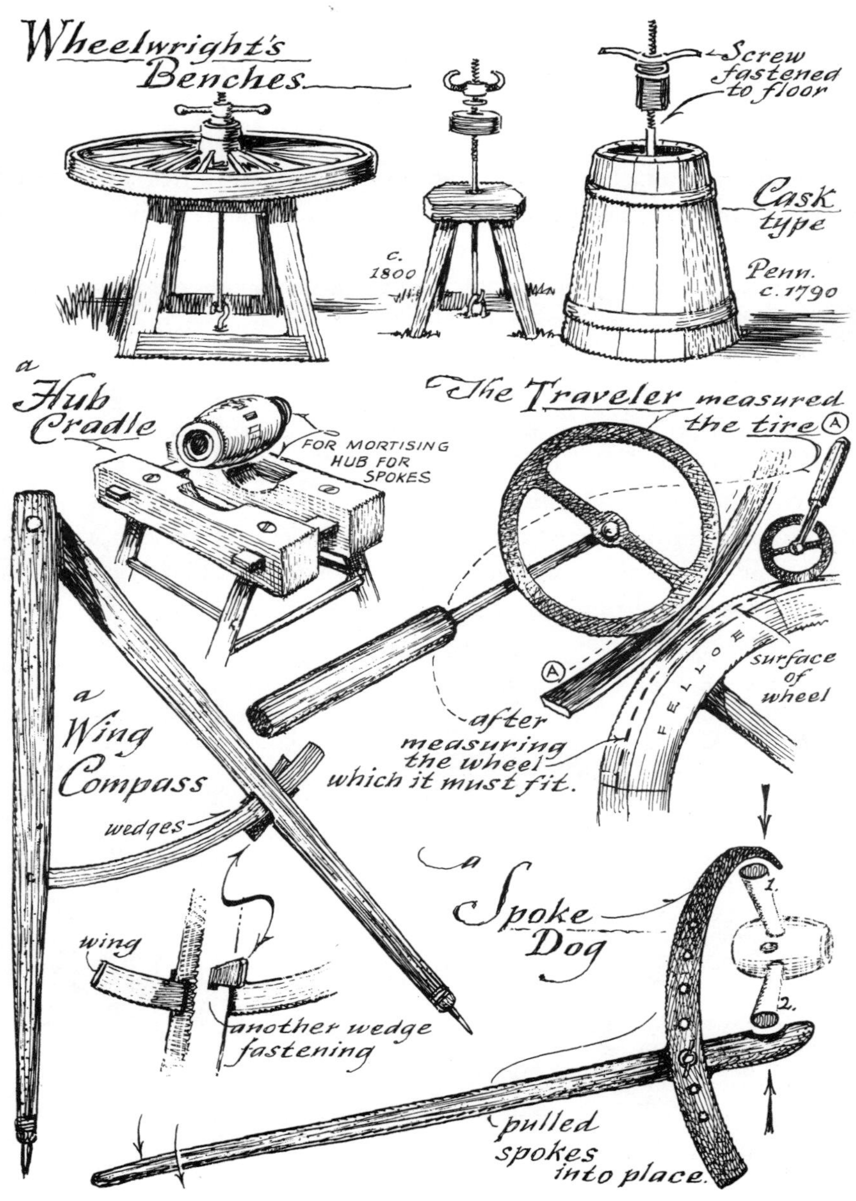
Wheelwright's Benches
Screw fastened to floor
Cask type
c. 1800
Penn. c. 1790
a Hub Cradle
FOR MORTISING HUB FOR SPOKES
The Traveler measured the tire Ⓐ
Ⓐ
surface of wheel
FELLOE
after measuring the wheel which it must fit.
a Wing Compass
wedges
wing
another wedge fastening
a Spoke Dog
1.
2.
pulled spokes into place.

It's all in the Way you Hit it.

Today we think a hammer is a hammer—the same thing that lays a roof, cracks a nut! But the early craftsman (like a good golfer) knew that *how* you hit and *what you hit with* could make a difference in the job being done. See, in the drawing below, how the flail separates the grain while the pestle grinds it; yet both tools hit.

The "flinting pick" did the job of making gun flints; the "bricklayer's hammer" and "axe" and "raker" did work that is still admired after two centuries. The "printing mallet" stamped designs on painted floor cloths (popular before linoleum). The "flood gate hammer" didn't smash the gate; its massive weight just moved it. The "zax" cut roofing slate and made nail holes in it. The "trunnel hammer" knocked trunnels in without smashing them. And so on. Each "hammer" hit a special kind of blow to do the specialty the craftsman needed done.

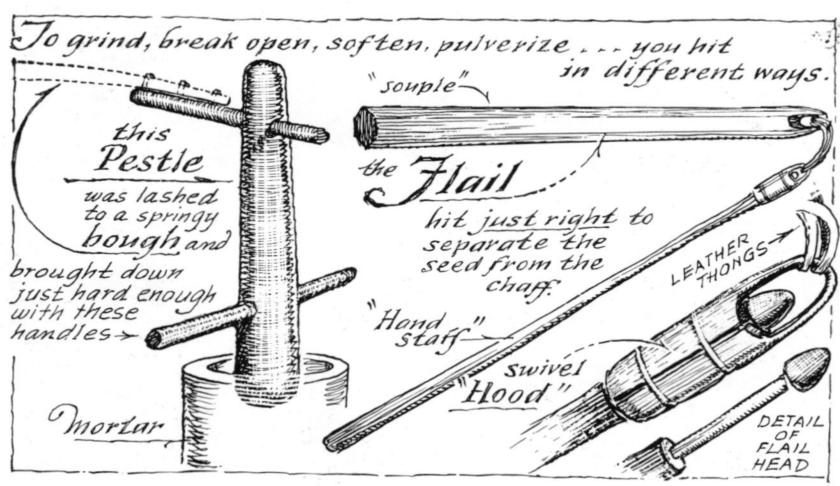
To grind, break open, soften, pulverize . . . you hit in different ways.
this Pestle was lashed to a springy bough and brought down just hard enough with these handles
Mortar
"souple"
the Flail
hit just right to separate the seed from the chaff.
"Hand staff"
swivel "Hood"
LEATHER THONGS
DETAIL OF FLAIL HEAD

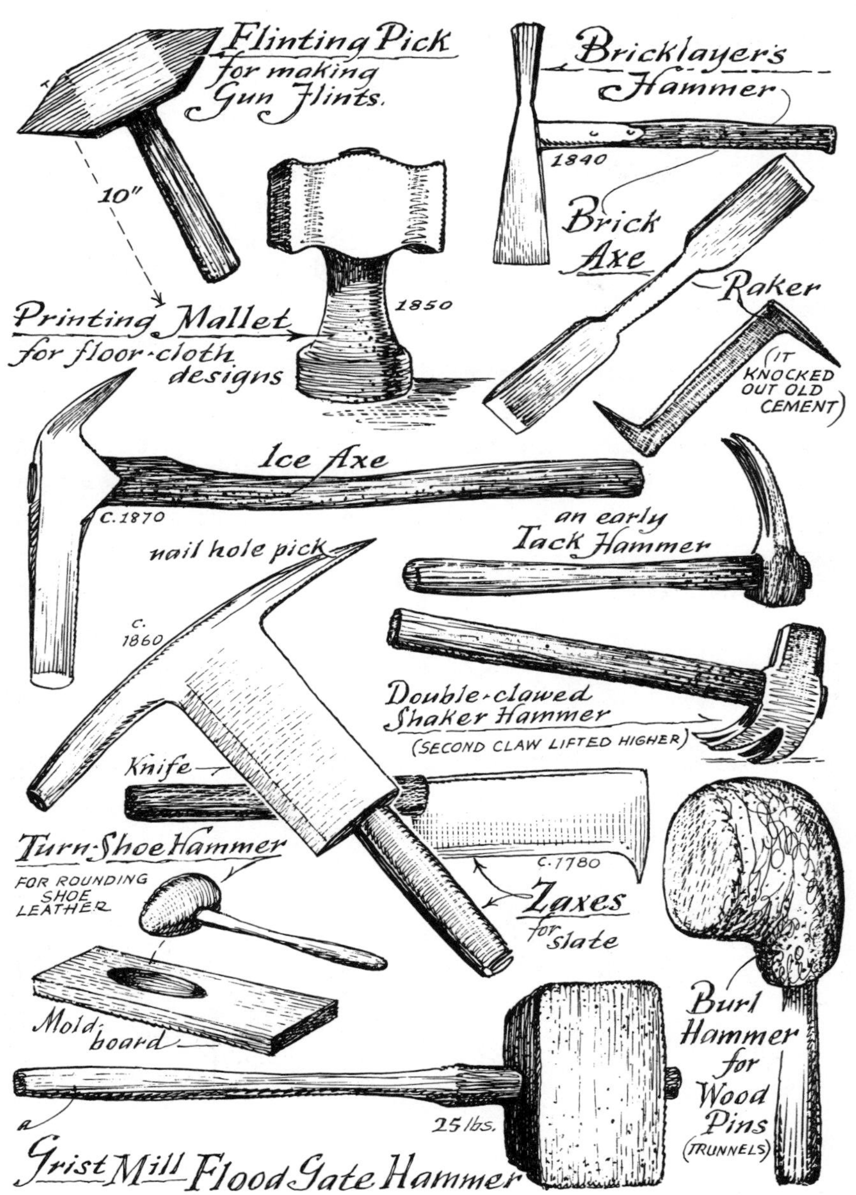
Flinting Pick for making Gun Flints.
10"
Bricklayer's Hammer
1840
Brick Axe
Raker
(IT KNOCKED OUT OLD CEMENT)
Printing Mallet for floor-cloth designs
1850
Ice Axe
C.1870
an early Tack Hammer
nail hole pick
C. 1860
Double-clawed Shaker Hammer
(SECOND CLAW LIFTED HIGHER)
Knife
Turn-Shoe Hammer
FOR ROUNDING SHOE LEATHER
C.1780
Zaxes for slate
Mold board
Burl Hammer for Wood Pins
(TRUNNELS)
25 lbs.
a Grist Mill Flood Gate Hammer

Hay Implements

Among the more plentiful old barn relics is the hay knife. Wide, heavy and with the blade on the outer edge, most people wonder how hay could be reaped with it. It didn't reap—it cut out portions of hay from the haystack. The hay-spade and hay-saw did the same thing. The hay-spade knife, however, doubled as pumpkin cutter in the days when pumpkins were animal food. Pumpkin stalks tended to choke animals, so pumpkins were cut from the top and the stalks destroyed.

The slender, sharp reaping hook became an American design of rare beauty by the late 1700's. But during the late 1800's the art of cutting gave way to the art of slashing, and a sickle is a better slasher. The earliest corn knife was machetelike, but the sicklelike corn knife appeared in the early 1800's.

The sickle reaped with the aid of a grass crook (hay crook), which was also used for pulling loose hay from the stack.

Although such serrations are usually worn away in ancient tools, the early sickles were usually serrated; this sets them apart from the slender reaping hook.

This Connecticut
Hay Knife
c. 1850
worked like a saw.

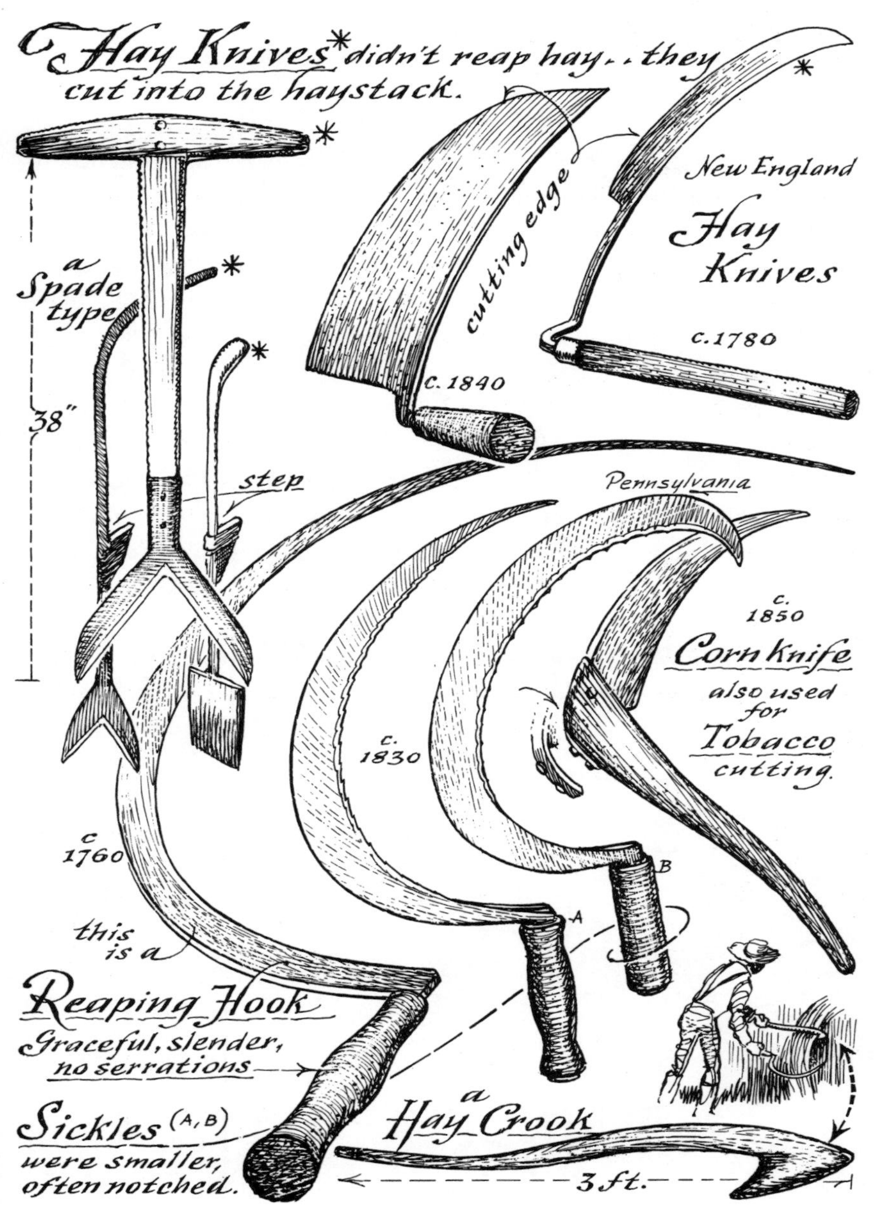
Hay Knives* didn't reap hay.. they cut into the haystack.
*
a Spade type
38"
*
*
step
cutting edge
c. 1840
*
New England Hay Knives
c. 1780
Pennsylvania
c. 1850
Corn knife
also used for Tobacco cutting.
c. 1830
c 1760
B
A
this is a
Reaping Hook
Graceful, slender, no serrations
Sickles (A, B)
were smaller, often notched.
a Hay Crook
3 ft.

Knives and Grass

The first American grass blades were from England and matched to naturally bent "snaths" (handles) without "nibs" (hand grips). Our early scythes and cradle scythes were things of rare grace. Even those of the 1800's that were factory-made retained the lines that made them different from the cruder European and English implements. The snath was usually made of willow, shaped in hot oil; the nibs and fingers of hickory; the sned of ash. Wire rods were added in the late 1800's.

The scythes and forks of America before the late 1800's will someday be prized as pieces of art, but as of now they are so large or cumbersome that few choose to collect them. You are almost never likely to see an ancient wooden rake or scythe broken, although those made during the last seventy-five years or so have an average life of about five to ten years.

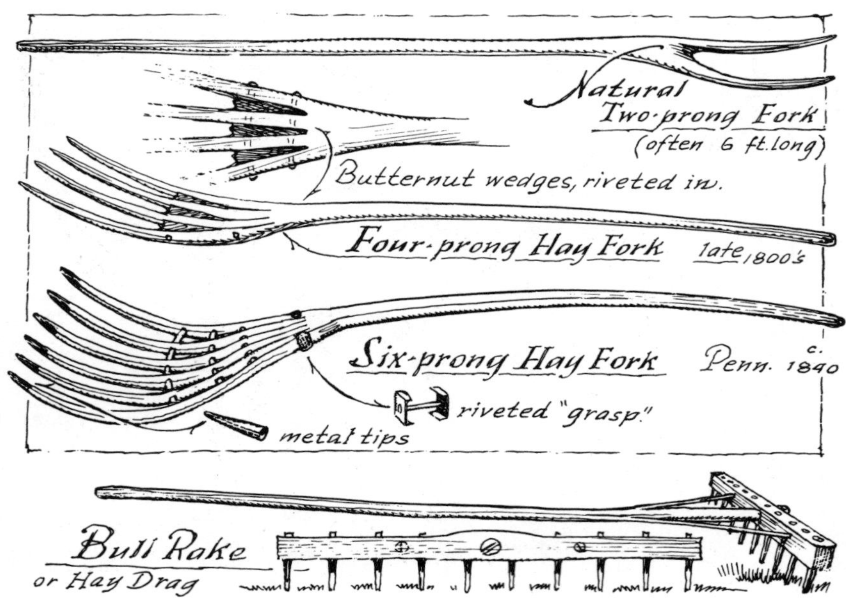

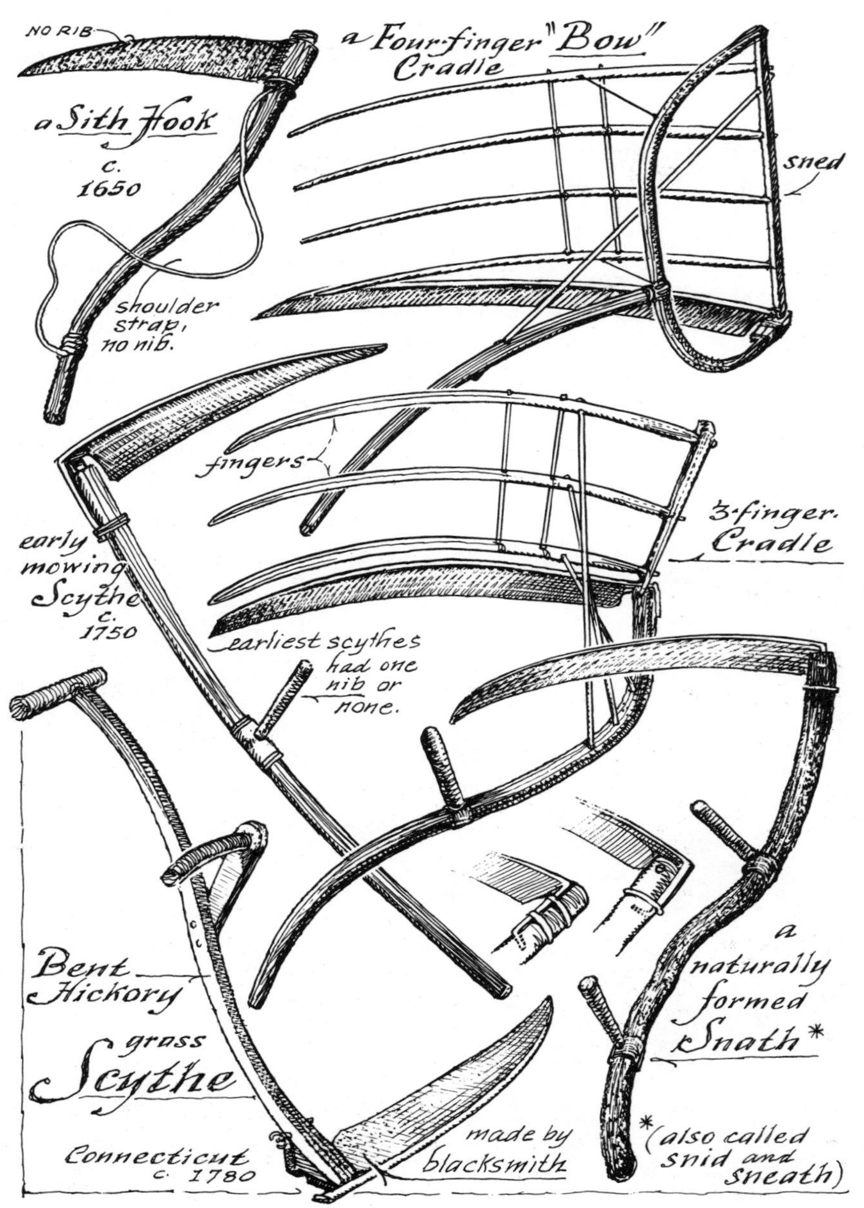
NO RIB
a Sith Hook
c. 1650
shoulder strap, no nib.
a Four-finger "Bow" Cradle
sned
fingers
3-finger Cradle
early mowing Scythe c. 1750
earliest scythes had one nib or none.
Bent Hickory grass Scythe
Connecticut c. 1780
made by blacksmith
a naturally formed Snath*
*(also called snid and sneath)

Found in the Barn

Oddities now, common items a century ago, here are a few things that were found in old barns and brought to me for identification. A tiny yoke for a goose, a cheesemaker's curd cutter and stirrer, a big winnowing scoop one used to throw flailed grain into the air to let the wind blow away the chaff—these are things that bring the past back vividly. Most old barns have eel spears tucked away near the rafters, although there may not be a river or lake for miles around. Yet a century ago men prized their swamp and wetlands, and stored up water in millponds for water-power instead of bulldozing over the wet places as we do now.

The American countryside was very different a century or two ago!

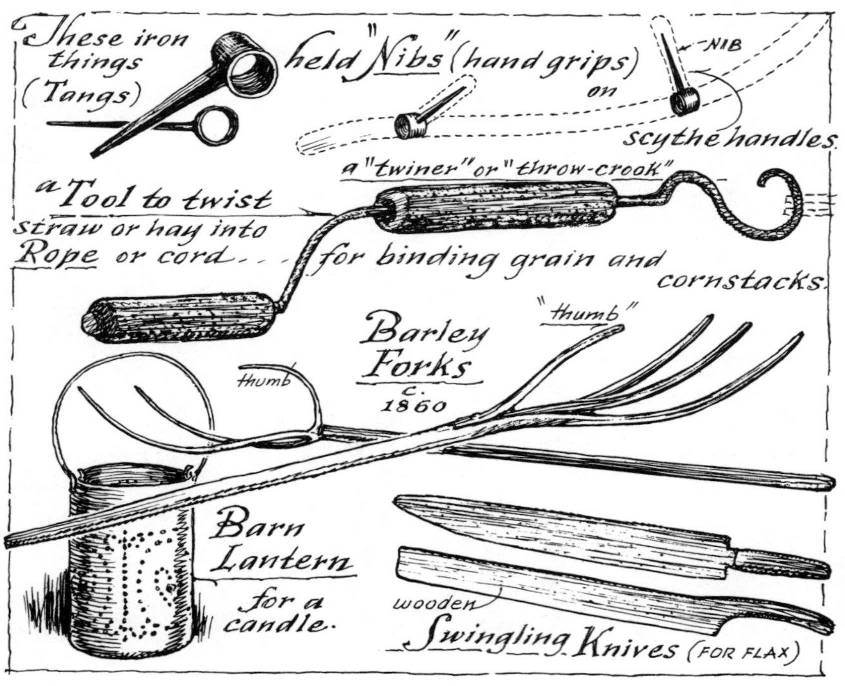
These iron things (Tangs)
held "Nibs" (hand grips) on
NIB
scythe handles.
a "twiner" or "throw-crook"
a Tool to twist straw or hay into Rope or cord...
for binding grain and cornstacks.
"thumb"
Barley Forks c. 1860
thumb
Barn Lantern
for a candle.
wooden
Swingling Knives (FOR FLAX)

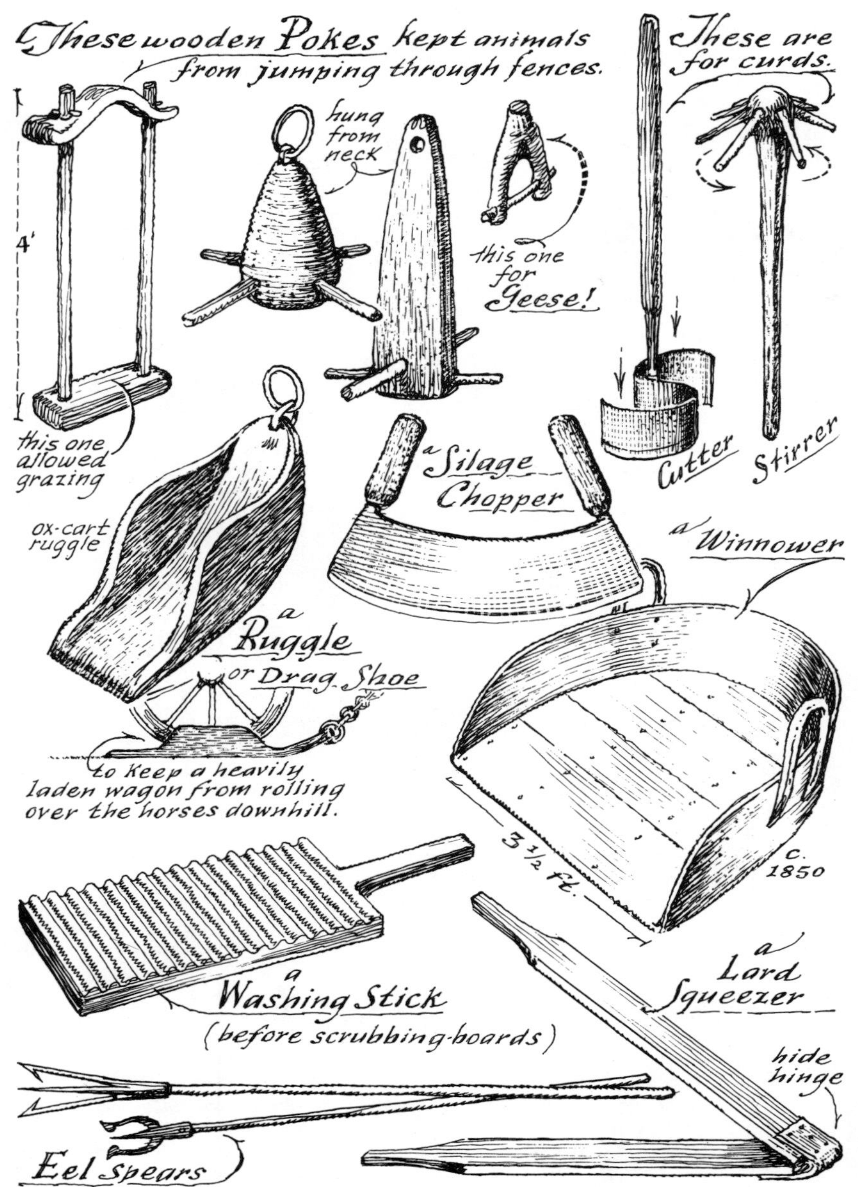
These wooden Pokes kept animals from jumping through fences.
4'
this one allowed grazing
hung from neck
this one for Geese!
These are for curds.
Cutter
Stirrer
a Silage Chopper
ox-cart ruggle
a Ruggle or Drag Shoe
to keep a heavily laden wagon from rolling over the horses downhill.
a Winnower
3 1/2 ft.
c. 1850
a Washing Stick
(before scrubbing-boards)
a Lard Squeezer
hide hinge
Eel Spears

Index

About the Author

ERIC SLOANE has written many books about Early American times and has collected for research purposes the tools, sometimes ingeniously devised, often exquisitely constructed, that our crafts-respecting forefathers made, with which they carved those delightful pieces and useful articles that made up the wonderful hand-made world of yesterday.

No worshiper of old things for the sake of age alone, Sloane collects only the good things of the past and tries to reintroduce the Early American philosophy of excellence to the present generation. Why would a backwoods farmer forge an axe with classic decorations on it? Where did the maker of this hand-made tool get his knowledge of Greek symmetry? Mr. Sloane enjoys describing those accomplishments of a proud and individualistic world, in the hope that the reader will remember something worthwhile that otherwise would be forgotten in this present world of rapid changes and mass production.

Look for the next illustrated title
by
Eric Sloane

A REVERENCE FOR WOOD

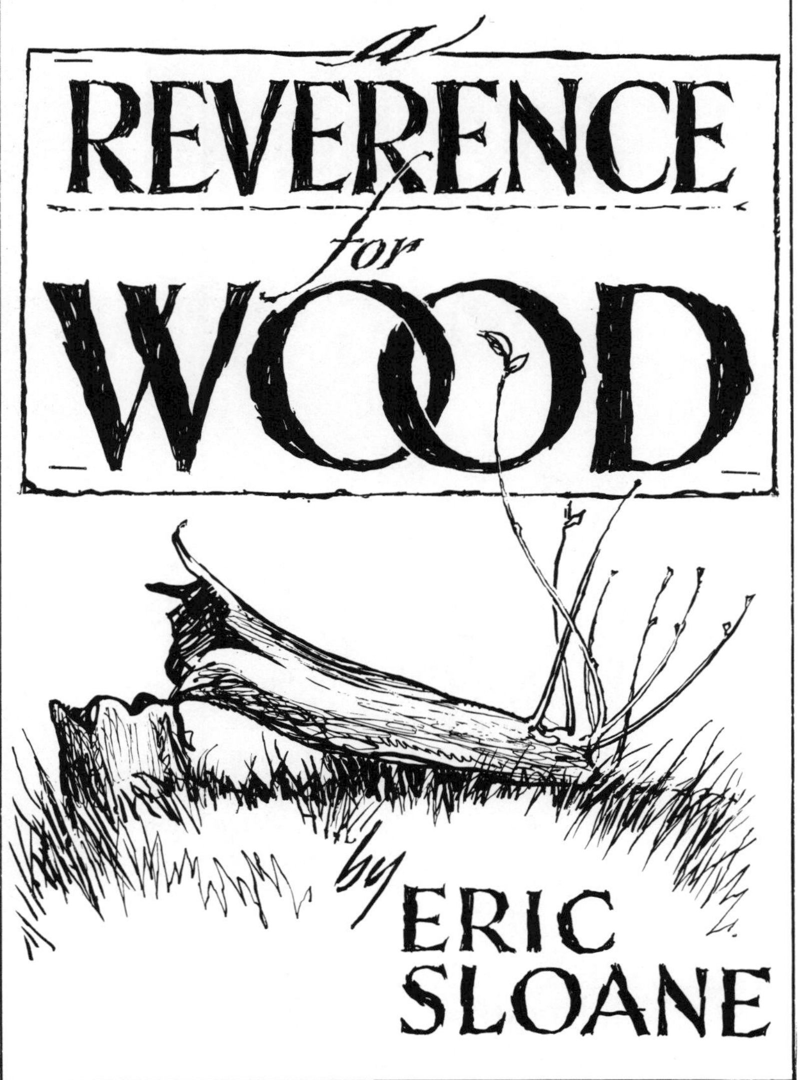

To be released by Ballantine Books

AVAILABLE NOW

A Ballantine Illustrated Book

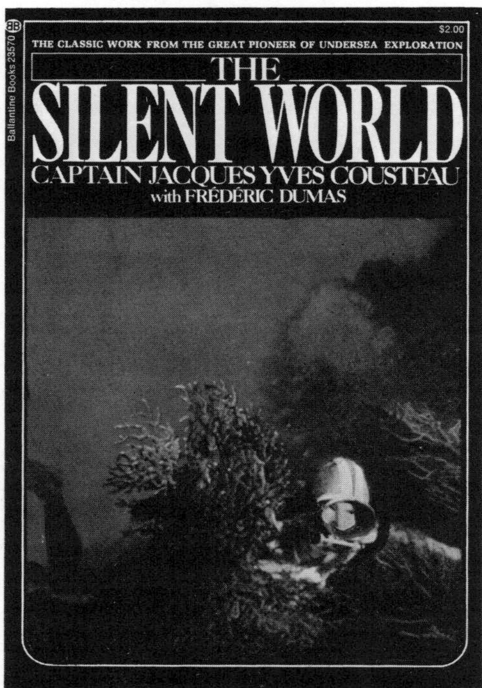

"We owe Captain Cousteau an immense debt of gratitude . . . The book makes a real contribution to our understanding of the world beneath the sea's surface."

—Rachel Carson

To order by mail, send $2.00 per book plus 25¢ per order for handling to Ballantine Cash Sales, P.O. Box 505, Westminster, Maryland 21157. Please allow three weeks for delivery.

Absolute Boyfriend

Story & Art by

Yuu Watase

Absolute Boyfriend

CAST

SOSHI ASAMOTO

NIGHT TENJO

GAKU NAMIKIRI

SATORI MIYABE

TOSHIKI & YUKI

STORY

DEPRESSED BY GETTING REJECTED, RIIKO BOUGHT NIGHT--THE IDEAL BOYFRIEND--ON A STRANGE WEBSITE. A KISS FROM RIIKO WON NIGHT'S DEVOTION, BUT TO MAKE HIS BOND TO HER PERMANENT THEY HAVE TO GO ALL THE WAY, AND RIIKO ISN'T SURE SHE'S READY. NEVERTHELESS, THE OPPORTUNITY TO CONSUMMATE THEIR RELATIONSHIP SOON ARRIVES IN THE FORM OF A GIFT CERTIFICATE FOR A FREE NIGHT'S STAY IN A FANCY HOTEL. BUT BEFORE THEY CAN PUT THEIR PLAN INTO ACTION, RIIKO'S PARENTS SHOW UP, AND HER FATHER IS FAR FROM PLEASED TO LEARN THAT HIS LITTLE GIRL HAS A BOYFRIEND. NIGHT FINALLY MANAGES TO WIN HER FATHER'S TEPID APPROVAL...FOR THEM TO BE "FRIENDS." BUT NOW THAT HER PARENTS HAVE LEFT AGAIN, WILL FRIENDSHIP TURN INTO SOMETHING MORE?

Act 19: First Crush

BE CAREFUL, RIIKO!!
AND THERE'D BETTER NOT BE ANY HANKY-PANKY!!
BE NICE TO EACH OTHER!
RIIKO, WHAT'S "HANKY-PANKY"?
...
MOM AND DAD WENT BACK TO WORK OVER-SEAS.
HOW-EVER ...
HANKY-PANKY!? FOR CRYING OUT LOUD!
Emergency tape job

MY POOR GIFT CERTIFICATE FOR A NIGHT'S STAY IN A HOTEL SUITE!
DAD SURE TORE IT UP GOOD.
SIGH
AND NOW WE'VE TOTALLY LOST OUR MOMENTUM!
NIGHT HASN'T EVEN BEEN TRYING TO GET ME TO HAVE SEX LATELY...
Out again today
IT'S A PAIN WHEN HE DOES, BUT...
...BEING IGNORED REALLY SUCKS. MAYBE I'LL DO SOME HOMEWORK.
MIXED FEEL-INGS
THUMP FWUMP
AAH!
OOPS...

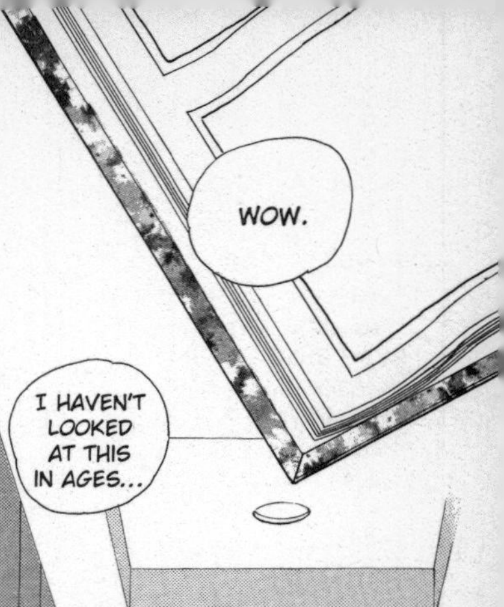
WOW.
I HAVEN'T LOOKED AT THIS IN AGES...

RIIKO, I'M HOME!

RIIKO?

HWOO
EEK!
SHIVER

NIGHT!!
Don't do that!
WHAP WHAP
WHAT WERE YOU LOOKING AT?

Hi, Watase here!! I was a zombie when I was working on Vol. 3, so my columns were a little flaky. Let's hope I'll do better this time. I was able to unwind a bit (it still wasn't enough!) at a convention in America in late May, so I feel a little better. Just a little. My friend and I wore yukata (informal cotton kimonos) the whole time, and tried to show off our Japaneseness. But a bunch of American girls were wearing yukata too, so we were upset because we didn't stand out at all! It was fun though. We went to the mall dressed that way and got a lot of attention there. Some people even took pictures of us. That was nice. It's not that easy to wear one, you know.

Anyway, I was swamped with work, but I went to see *Lord of the Rings: Return of the King*! I'm so glad I was able to catch it while it was still in theaters!!! A TV screen just wouldn't do it justice!! It was so majestic and moving, I was blown away!! It even made me rethink the way I live my life. I'm SO going to buy the DVD!! This is the real deal! So many movies these days are just eye-candy with no substance, but this one has vision and philosophy and profundity!! What an epic!! And Sam!! Samwise Gamgee, you're incredible!! He's the best. If you haven't seen it yet, I highly recommend it--you'll get something truly satisfying!!

Pant, pant... DVDs only cost $15 in the States. That's so cheap! Things are too expensive in Japan!

THIS? IT'S MY OLD PHOTO ALBUM FROM GRADE SCHOOL.
YOUR PHOTO ALBUM?

THIS IS ME AND SOSHI!
Wow.
YOU'RE SO LITTLE!
THAT'S RIGHT, HUMANS START OFF AS BABIES, DON'T THEY?

OH YEAH, NIGHT NEVER HAD A CHILD-HOOD...
YOU'RE SO CUTE!

HEY...
WHO'S THIS? HE'S IN A PICTURE BY HIMSELF.
Oh... HIM?
Heh Heh
HE WAS MY FIRST CRUSH!
WHAT!?
THAT'S TOSHIKI MURA-KAMI.
HE WAS A YEAR OLDER AND REALLY COOL! HE WAS ATHLETIC AND SMART AND REALLY NICE...
Imagi-nation
BUT HE WAS IN A DIFFERENT GRADE, SO I NEVER GOT A CHANCE TO TALK TO HIM, AND THEN HE MOVED AWAY.

THIS SURE BRINGS BACK MEMORIES...
FWOOSH
ARE THOSE FLAMES OF JEALOUSY!?
Toshiki...
I'M ALREADY JEALOUS OF SOSHI.
THESE OTHER GUYS SHARE MEMORIES WITH YOU...
IT WAS A LONG TIME AGO.
IT'S STILL FRUSTRAT-ING!
NIGHT...
I know!
WE CAN MAKE LOTS OF NEW MEMORIES!
REALLY!?
OKAY, LET'S GO ON A DATE TOMORROW AND MAKE SOME SWEET MEMORIES TOGETHER!!
WHAT!?

YOUR DAD RIPPED UP THE GIFT CERTIFICATE ...
BUT I'VE BEEN WORKING SO I COULD PAY FOR A SUITE MYSELF!
In a cheaper hotel.
WE CAN FINALLY HAVE A ROMANTIC NIGHT TOGETHER! ♥

I'M NERVOUS, BUT NIGHT IS SO SWEET.
HE DID ALL THIS FOR ME.
TONIGHT WE'RE FINALLY GOING TO BECOME LOVERS.

ZING

OUCH!!

ARE YOU ALL RIGHT, RIIKO?

TOO MUCH WALKING, I GUESS.

Darn it.

I SHOULDN'T HAVE WORN HIGH HEELS!

THROB THROB

TMP

YOU OKAY? DID YOU HURT YOUR ANKLE?

BA-BUMP
YOU CAN USE THIS COMPRESS, IF YOU WANT.
DO I... KNOW THIS GUY?
HERE, LET ME.
HE LOOKS FAMILIAR...
TOSHIKI!!

OKAY! COMING!
Er...
THANK YOU!
LET'S GET GOING!
NO PROBLEM.
OH!
IT'S TOSHIKI!

WAIT!
ZING
The other ankle
YEEOWW!!
HERE, I BOUGHT YOU SOME LESS DANGEROUS FOOT-WEAR.
THROB
THROB
YOU SURE YOU'RE OKAY!?
I... I'M FINE...
Thanks.
I'M SO LAME--LITERALLY.

I THOUGHT WE COULD GO ON THE FERRIS WHEEL AFTER DINNER.
I GUESS THAT'S OUT NOW.
WHAT? NO WAY! I WANNA GO!!
We have to!!
OKAY, OKAY.
If you insist.
WHEN WE GET TO OUR ROOM ...
I'LL GIVE YOUR ANKLES A GOOD MASSAGE.
GULP
THAT'S RIGHT... WE'RE GOING TO MAKE LOVE TONIGHT. ♡
THAT GUY LOOKED SO MUCH LIKE TOSHIKI...

Wow!
IT'S BEAUTI-FUL!
THIS PLACE IS CROWDED TOO.
LET'S WAIT IN LINE!!
HOW ARE YOUR ANKLES? WANT ME TO CARRY YOU?
I'M FINE!
BLUSH
PFFT
!!
OH, SORRY.
WHAT A CUTE COUPLE.

THANKS FOR THE COMPRESS.
YES, THANK YOU.
HOW'S YOUR ANKLE?
MUCH BETTER!
HE'S A DEAD RINGER FOR TOSHIKI!
GRIN
IT'S GOT TO BE HIM!
BUT WAIT ...
Frustrated because she can't ask his identity in front of Night
MWAP MWAP
RIIKO, YOU LOOK LIKE A GOLDFISH.
YUKI?
TOSHIKI ...
TUG
WHAT'S WRONG, YUKI?
MY STOMACH HURTS. I NEED TO GO TO THE BATH-ROOM...

YOU WANT ME TO GO WITH YOU!?
NO! YOU KEEP OUR PLACE IN LINE!
I WANNA GO ON THE FERRIS WHEEL !!
YEAH, BUT...
...
I'LL TAKE YOU!
WHUP
WHOA!
NIGHT !?
IT'S ONLY FAIR, AFTER WHAT YOU DID FOR US.
I'LL BE RIGHT BACK. YOU STAY IN LINE TOO, RIIKO!

SHOOM
BUT I FEEL BAD ...
WOW, HE'S FAST.
...
Glance
UM...
NOW'S MY CHANCE!
ARE YOU... RIIKO? RIIKO IZAWA?
MAYBE I'VE MISTAKEN YOU FOR SOMEONE ELSE, BUT...

YES!!
YES, I AM!!
AND YOU'RE TOSHIKI MURAKAMI! WE WENT TO GRADE SCHOOL TOGETHER!
I KNEW I'D SEEN YOU BEFORE!
...YEAH.
WOW! HOW HAVE YOU BEEN!?
ARE YOU OKAY?
Humans are so incon-venient.
UM...

IT'S BEEN A WHILE. IT'LL BE OUR TURN ON THE FERRIS WHEEL SOON.
I'M SORRY. YOU DON'T HAVE TO WAIT FOR ME.

THAT'S OKAY! WANT ME TO GET YOU SOME MEDICINE?

YES, PLEASE ...

THEY'RE STILL NOT BACK AND WE'RE NEXT!

...

GRIP

HUH?

LET'S GO TOGETHER!
WHAT!? BUT...
IT'LL BE FUN TO CATCH UP WITH EACH OTHER!
WE'LL GO AGAIN WITH THEM WHEN THEY GET BACK.
There's no use standing around.
NIGHT, I'M SORRY!!
Stomach-ache?
This should help.
I hope it works fast.

ISN'T IT BEAUTI-FUL?
YEAH ...
WOOO
REMEM-BER THE OTHER TIME...
...YOU HELPED ME WITH MY ANKLE?
I TWISTED MY ANKLE IN THE RELAY ON SPORTS DAY.
AND YOU TOOK ME TO THE NURSE'S OFFICE...
...BUT THE NURSE WASN'T THERE, SO YOU BANDAGED IT FOR ME YOURSELF.

OH!
THAT WAS WHEN I FELL FOR YOU...

NO!! YOU DIDN'T HEAR THAT!!
...

WOOO
UH-OH. NOW IT'S WEIRD.

IS IT OVER YET?

Hey!
IS THAT NIGHT DOWN THERE?
I NEVER ...
...FORGOT YOU, EITHER.

OH...

OH !?
Hey!
RIIKO!
TOSHIKI !!
SORRY WE TOOK SO LONG.
No problem.
THANKS FOR TAKING CARE OF MY BROTHER!
TOSHIKI, YOU RODE IT ALREADY? NO FAIR!
We'll just get back in line.
RIIKO?

SEE YOU AROUND ...
RIIKO!
HUH?
RETURNS TO HER SENSES
NO...
NO WAY!

WHAT'S WRONG? YOU'RE ACTING STRANGE.

WHY?

WHY?

NO, I'M FINE. REALLY.

Acting very suspi-ciously

You're different.

ANYWAY, I'LL GO CHECK US IN.

WHAT SHOULD I DO?

THIS WAS GOING TO BE OUR BIG NIGHT.

HE WAS MY FIRST CRUSH, BUT... WHAT HAVE I DONE?

I CAN'T TELL NIGHT. IT WAS JUST AN ACCIDENT!

I'll forget it ever happened!

PAT
HEY!
WHAT A COINCIDENCE. YOU GUYS ARE STAYING HERE TOO?
GIVE YOUR BOYFRIEND THE SLIP...
...AND COME UP TO MY ROOM.
WHAT !?
THIS CAN'T BE HAPPENING ...
Hey.
I'VE GOT AN IDEA.

Absolute
Boyfriend

Act 20: A Big Problem

GIVE YOUR BOY-FRIEND THE SLIP...
...AND COME UP TO MY ROOM.
WHAT !?
I-I ...!!
TOSHIKI !?
WHAT'S HE THINKING !?
I'M NOT THAT EASY!!
UM...

NO THANKS!!
HEY...
WHAT'S WRONG, RIIKO?
WIP
WHEEZE WHEEZE
L-LET'S GO TO OUR ROOM!!

NOW!!

WOW, HOW EAGER!

Is she that aroused already!?

BIG MISUNDER-STANDING

I'M IN ENOUGH TROUBLE FOR LETTING *THAT* HAPPEN!!

BA-BUMP BA-BUMP

DO YOU WANT TO TAKE A SHOWER FIRST?

WHAT?
OR SHALL WE TAKE ONE TOGETHER?
N-NO, YOU GO AHEAD!!
SWUFF
BA-BUMP
MY RING IS GOING CRAZY. YOU MUST BE NERVOUS.
FWASH
DON'T WORRY.
I'LL BE GENTLE.
BA-BUMP

NIGHT
...
GET A GRIP, RIIKO. WHO CARES ABOUT AN OLD CRUSH?
I WILL BREAK AWAY FROM MY CHILDHOOD TONIGHT!!
What the heck am I talking about?
BEEP BEEP BEEP
URK
BEEP BEEP BEEP
COULD IT BE THE FRONT DESK?
BUT WE HAVEN'T ORDERED ANY-THING.
Now what?
RIIKO? IT'S ME, TOSHIKI.
GACK
HOW'D HE GET MY ROOM NUMBER !?

SORRY ABOUT EARLIER.

IS HE SORRY FOR INVITING ME TO HIS ROOM, OR FOR KISSING ME?

BLUSH

IT'S JUST THAT I HAD A CRUSH ON YOU TOO...

I WANT TO MAKE IT UP TO YOU. CAN YOU COME TO MY ROOM, JUST FOR A MINUTE?

WHAT !?

YOUR BOYFRIEND MIGHT THINK IT WAS WEIRD IF I CAME TO SEE YOU.

DON'T WORRY, MY BROTHER IS HERE WITH ME.

BUT ...

PLEASE, FOR OLD TIME'S SAKE?

In this volume, Riiko goes to Odaiba. My editor and I went there to take some reference pictures. We were only there at night, but it was fun. It seemed kind of pathetic for two women to go on the Ferris wheel together, though. The PA system was too loud. (smile) It didn't seem very romantic. But does that matter?
I wished I could hang out all day at Venus Fort, just window-shopping and stuff. And then I got hooked on the Daiba Mall where they've recreated the '50s-style shops and working-class back streets of the "Low City." I love traditional Japanese stuff, so I spent a lot of time wandering around there. Unfortunately, we didn't get to go to Little Hong Kong. I'll go there next time! Sigh...

I was walking in the train station by myself after my editor and I went our separate ways. Everything was so ultra-modern and no one was around because it was late at night. I felt a little uneasy. What if something weird were to happen...!? Yeah, right. But what's the point of making things so excessively big? Is it just me, or does it feel like a huge waste of space?

There are so many places I haven't been to yet. I'd better make more time to enjoy life.

KLAK

HEY.

H...

HI!

COME IN, COME IN!

HAVE A SEAT. WANT SOMETHING TO DRINK?

HUH?

WHERE'S YOUR BROTHER?

YUKI?
HE WENT OUT TO EXPLORE THE HOTEL.
WHAT!?

WE'RE ALONE!! OH NO...

OUR PARENTS BOTH WORK, SO WE HAVEN'T BEEN ABLE TO GO ANYWHERE FOR A VACATION THIS YEAR.

YUKI KEPT PESTER-ING ME TO TAKE HIM SOME-WHERE.
NOW I'M GLAD I DID.
I GOT TO SEE YOU AGAIN.
UM, I'M NOT UPSET ABOUT WHAT HAPPENED !!
SCURRY
WELL, GOOD-BYE!
WHAT? HOLD ON! YOU JUST GOT HERE!
I HAVE TO GO! MY BOY-FRIEND IS WAITING!!
HEH
YOUR BOY-FRIEND, HUH?

WHAT THE...

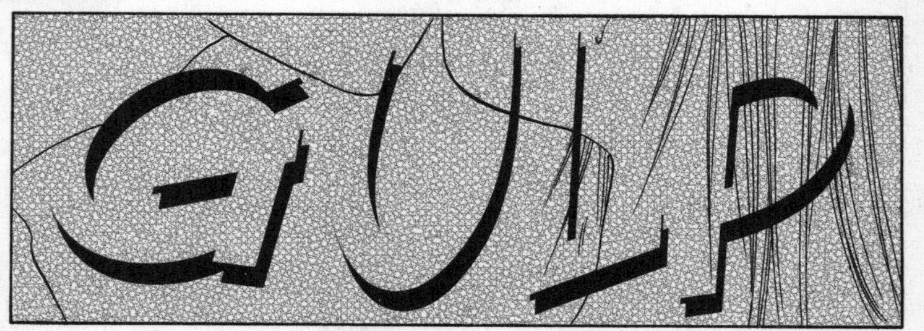

WHAT?
SWOOn
HUH ...?
SWUMP
I'M BETTER THAN HE IS.

Dear Night,
I'll be right back.
Riiko
WHERE COULD SHE HAVE GONE?
RIIKO !?
Huh?
RIIKO !?

HERE'S LOOKING AT YOU, KID.

RIIKO!?

SPLOOSH

WHERE'S HE GOING?

BOSS!! WE'RE GETTING REPORTS OF A NAKED MAN RUNNING AROUND THE HOTEL!!

WHAT!?

RI...

STOP!

YOU SICKO!!

VOOM

ACK!?

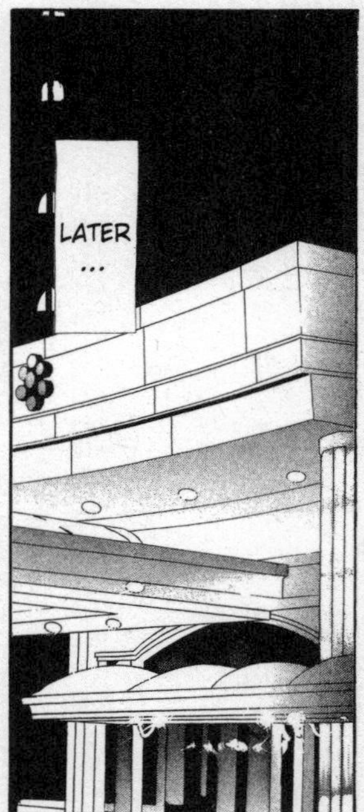

Ahh.
I SURE GOT YELLED AT.
AT LEAST THEY DIDN'T KICK US OUT. BUT I STILL HAVEN'T FOUND RIIKO.

Oh!

RIIKO !?

HEY!
YOUR DOOR WAS OPEN, SO I CAME IN!
AREN'T YOU...
I'M YUKI! THANKS FOR GETTING ME THE MEDICINE TODAY!
YOU'RE LOOKING FOR YOUR GIRL-FRIEND, RIGHT?
WELL, I KNOW WHERE SHE IS!
WHERE!?
COME CLOSER! LISTEN ...

576667♥
432836♪
8#75337.
WHIRR
THUD

HEH
UH...
WHERE AM I?
AND WHY AM I...
...NAKED !?
GOOD MORNING.

WHAT THE HECK?
DOOM
LAST NIGHT...
...WAS WONDERFUL.
!!

AGH!
GOODBYE!!
IS THIS REAL!?
TELL ME THIS DIDN'T HAPPEN!!
WHY!? HOW!?
WHAT'LL I DO NOW!?
WHAT'LL I TELL NIGHT!?
1511
PLEASE LET THIS BE A DREAM!!

WIP

AAAH!!

NIGHT!! WAKE UP!!

IS THIS BECAUSE I HAD SEX WITH ANOTHER GUY!? I DON'T EVEN WANT TO THINK ABOUT IT!!

SHAKE SHAKE SHAKE

BLIP

6:00

BLINK

UM.
PLIP PLIP
I CAME RIGHT BACK.
PLIP PLIP
LIAR

I CAME BACK AND YOU WERE ASLEEP.
(This part is true.)
HA HA HA
WHAT!? I FELL ASLEEP !?

WHERE'S YUKI!? HE WAS GOING TO TELL ME WHERE YOU WERE...
?

OOF
OH WELL! WE CAN START NOW!
THW
AP

I'M SORRY, NIGHT. I WANT TO GO HOME.
WHAT !?
RIIKO... ARE YOU MAD AT ME?
NO, NIGHT ...
AAAAGH
!!
YOU SHOULD BE MAD AT ME!!
I JUST WANT TO GET OUT OF HERE!!
HOW DID THIS HAPPEN !?

SECOND SEMESTER STARTS TODAY.
HAGGARD
She is angry.
I FEEL HORRIBLE.
DID I REALLY HAVE SEX WITH TOSHIKI?
She goes to school first.
I DON'T REMEMBER ANYTHING.
EIBA HIGH SCHOOL
NIGHT CAN TELL THAT SOME-THING IS WRONG.
THIS IS HORRIBLE ...

...EVEN IF HE WAS MY FIRST CRUSH!
THIS CAN'T BE RIGHT!!
SURE IT IS.

WHAT A COINCI-DENCE, YET AGAIN!!
RIIKO, YOU GO TO THIS SCHOOL?

TMP TMP TMP TMP TMP TMP

IT MUST BE FATE...

HM?

WAS THAT RIIKO?

WHAT ARE YOU DOING HERE!?

I TRANS-FERRED. WE JUST MOVED TO THIS AREA.

THIS IS GREAT! I REALLY WANTED TO FIND YOU!

IT WOULD'VE BEEN A BAD THING FOR US TO PART LIKE THAT.
UGH!
"Us"?!

WE'RE LOVERS NOW...
...AREN'T WE?
YOUR BOY-FRIEND DOESN'T MATTER ANYMORE.

I'LL BE SEEING YOU...
...MY RIIKO.
...
WHAT AM I GOING TO DO?
THANK-FULLY NIGHT WASN'T WITH ME...
GACK!
WHO'S THAT GUY?

HUFF HUFF

SOB SOB

WHAT WAS THAT FOR!?

DO YOU REMEMBER TOSHIKI MURAKAMI FROM GRADE SCHOOL?

HE WAS A YEAR AHEAD OF US.

YEAH.

I MET HIM AT AN OFFLINE GET-TOGETHER.

BA-DOOM

A WHAT?
FOR THE PERIOD DRAMA SOCIETY WEBSITE, TO DISCUSS THE FUTURE OF PERIOD DRAMA.
WHAT'S TO DISCUSS!?
IT WAS WEIRD TO RUN INTO HIM AFTER ALL THESE YEARS, BUT WE TALKED FOR A WHILE.
HE'S CHANGED A LOT. I TOOK A PICTURE OF HIM.
BIP

SH25US
DoCoNo
WHO THE HELL IS THAT!?
TOSHIKI MURA-KAMI.
But...
THAT CAN'T BE HIM!!
No way!
PEOPLE CHANGE IN FIVE YEARS.
THIS IS TOSHIKI MURA-KAMI!?
THEN...
...WHO'S THAT GUY!?

Absolute
Boyfriend

Act 21: Secret

WHAT THE HECK !?
...WASN'T TOSHIKI MURAKAMI, MY FIRST CRUSH!?
THE GUY WHO KISSED ME-- AND WHO I MAY EVEN HAVE SLEPT WITH...
TOSHIKI MURA-KAMI: 5 YEARS AGO
TOSHIKI MURA-KAMI: PRESENT DAY
SEIBA HIGH SCHOOL

TOSHIKI MURAKAMI IS SOME OTHER GUY.
THEN WHO IS HE!?
...
MY NAME'S TOSHIKI TOO...
TOSHIKI *SHIRA-SAKI*.
SHIRA-SAKI !?
THEN, WHY DID YOU SAY...
"AND YOU'RE TOSHIKI MURAKAMI! WE WENT TO GRADE SCHOOL TOGETHER!"
"...YEAH."
OH, THAT?

I THOUGHT YOU WERE FLIRTING WITH ME.
YOU'RE CUTE SO I WENT ALONG WITH IT.
WHAT!?

I HAD THE SAME NAME AS YOUR FIRST CRUSH.

IT SEEMED LIKE FATE...

AND THAT GAVE YOU THE RIGHT TO KISS ME!?

And... whatever else...

IT WASN'T SO BAD, WAS IT?

YOU DIDN'T SEEM TO MIND AT THE TIME.

GASP

ARE YOU SURE YOU LOVE YOUR BOY-FRIEND?

O-OF COURSE I DO!

REALLY?

MAYBE YOU JUST WANT ATTENTION FROM ANYBODY.
SO I THOUGHT, WHY NOT ME?
AND WE'VE SPENT THE NIGHT TOGETHER NOW.
...
D-DID WE REALLY... GO ALL THE WAY?

I'D LIKE TO KEEP SEEING YOU.
I WONDER WHAT YOUR BOYFRIEND WOULD SAY IF HE FOUND OUT ABOUT US.
SHARR
I-B
RIIKO HAS BEEN ACTING WEIRD EVER SINCE THAT NIGHT AT THE HOTEL.
IS IT BECAUSE I FELL ASLEEP ON SUCH AN IMPORTANT NIGHT?
BUT WHY DID I FALL ASLEEP?

WHAT DID YUKI SAY TO ME? AND WHY ISN'T IT IN MY MEMORY CIRCUITS?
His brain
HEY, NIGHT.
IS EVERY-THING OKAY WITH YOU AND RIIKO?
Ack!
WHY DO YOU ASK!?
SHE'S ACTING WEIRD.
I SAW HER WITH A SECOND-YEAR. A GUY.
HUH?
AND SHE KEPT TALKING ABOUT SOMEONE WE KNEW BACK IN GRADE SCHOOL.
SHAPE UP! YOU'RE HER BOY-FRIEND!!
You still don't have my seal of approval, by the way!
...

SERIOUSLY, WHAT SHOULD I DO?
CAN I REALLY KEEP THIS FROM NIGHT?
MAYBE YOU JUST WANT ATTENTION FROM ANYBODY.
KNOCK KNOCK
RIIKO, THE BATH IS READY.
OKAY. THANKS.
STAGGER STAGGER
RIIKO ...

WHO WAS THAT GUY YOU WERE TALKING TO?
HALT
KRAK
SOSHI SAW YOU WITH HIM.
HE WANTED TO START A STUDENT FORUM! YEAH, THAT'S IT!!
JUST YOU AND HIM?
THAT'S RIGHT!!
And I just did the splits.
OKAY.
IF YOU SAY SO, I TRUST YOU.
THROB
HOW CAN I KEEP LYING TO HIM?
THE GUILT HURTS.

I DON'T EVEN REMEMBER THE NIGHT I SPENT WITH HIM. BUT STILL, WE...
RIIKO, YOU'RE SO PRETTY...
NOOOO!
KA-BAM

At first, Toshiki was going to be the "childhood friend" character before I came up with Soshi. He turned out quite a bit different from the rough sketches I did of him though. But I didn't want him to go to waste. But Yuki was the one the fans like most!! I think. Little boys can be so cute. But it would be boring if he were just a kid. It's much easier to work with characters that have quirky personalities.

So, I put them both on the cover of this volume. I'd intended to follow the trend of having one character on the cover, but... On the other hand, the two of them and the title Absolute Boyfriend could suggest another genre altogether. I realized this too late. Oh well.

Childhood friends show up a lot in manga, but that never seems to happen in real life! Especially ones who are good-looking guys. My family lived in Kobe when I was a baby, and a neighborhood boy and I used to play together a lot. One time his little brother looked at him and asked, "Are you going to marry her when you grow up?" Sounds like a sweet, heartwarming story. Oh, maybe I'll use it in a manga someday! He's probably middle-aged by now. (Sorry.)

DONG DONG
WOBBLE
IT'S HORRIBLE.
I'M SO STRESSED OUT...
ADULTERY.
KRASH WHAM
IT'S WRITTEN ALL OVER YOUR FACE, IZAWA.
TMP TMP
MIYABE!? ARE YOU TRYING TO GIVE ME A HEART ATTACK!?
RIIKO? ARE YOU OKAY?

...

TMP TMP TMP

HOLD ON.

DON'T TRY TO AVOID ME.

I MEANT WHAT I SAID BEFORE.

WHAP

NIGHT !?
YOU'RE THE GUY !?
HEY! THANKS FOR TAKING CARE OF MY LITTLE BROTHER THE OTHER DAY!
WHAT ARE YOU DOING TO RIIKO!?
UH-OH!
YOU SHOULD ASK HER.
RIGHT, RIIKO?
URK

I'D BETTER GO.
SEE YOU AROUND!

SILENCE

...

BLINK

POKE
C'MON, RIIKO!
DON'T BE SO SAD. I'M NOT UPSET.
LET'S EAT. YOU'LL FEEL BETTER!
OH, NIGHT ...
URGH
Hmm...
THIS NEEDS MORE SAUCE.
NIGHT!
I CAN'T!
I CAN'T HOLD IT IN ANY LONGER!
NIGHT!!

I...
I SLEPT WITH HIM!!
I WENT TO HIS ROOM THAT NIGHT...
I DON'T REMEMBER WHAT HAPPENED AFTER THAT...
BUT I WOKE UP IN HIS BED.

I'M SORRY!
I'M SO SORRY !!
WHY?
WASN'T I...
...A GOOD ENOUGH BOYFRIEND FOR YOU?

NO!
DOES THIS MEAN ...
...YOU DON'T NEED ME ANY-MORE?
THAT'S NOT IT!
IT'S NOT!
BUT I HAVE NO RIGHT TO ASK HIM TO STAY NOW.
...
...

OKAY.
SMILE
TMP
TMP
SHUP
KA-
CHAK

NIGHT!!
Huh?
NIGHT, IS THAT YOU?
I DON'T THINK... I'M WANTED ANYMORE.
HUH !?
WHAT'S WRONG? THAT'S CRAZY TALK!
I FAILED AS A LOVER FIGURE, SO COULD THE COMPANY TAKE ME BACK?
HELLO, GAKU?
WAIT... I DON'T GET IT!!
Hold on, Miss, I'm still eating that parfait!
LATER.
KLIK

TMP
RIIKO ...

WWWWWWWWWWOOM

KA-THWAK
YOU HUNG UP ON ME!! I TOLD YOU TO WAIT!!

SWF
NIGHT, I COULDN'T ASK YOU TO STAY.
I DON'T DESERVE YOU.

OH!
DING DONG
DING DONG
CHAK
...!!
ARE YOU SERIOUS !?

RIIKO DUMPED YOU?
STAGGER
I GUESS I'M NOT GOOD ENOUGH FOR HER.
CRAP!
IF THE MERCHANDISE I SOLD GETS RETURNED, IT'LL WRECK MY BONUS!!
AAGH
GUESS I'D BETTER CONTACT MY MANAGER.
WHAT IF THEY CUT MY SALARY?
SHAKE SHAKE
Too nervous
HELLO?
BOSS?
RIIKO ...

REALLY!? THEN IF WE COULD FIND ANOTHER BUYER...

TWITCH

THROB

OKAY, I'LL TAKE HIM BACK TO THE COMPANY FOR NOW.

NO.

WHAT?
I'VE CHANGED MY MIND.

I LOVE RIIKO!!
I'M THE ONLY BOY-FRIEND FOR HER!!
SHO OM
Um...
HEY!
BOSS, 01 JUST TOOK OFF! I'M GOING AFTER HIM!
DON'T BOTHER.

FWASH
MR. SHIRA-SAKI!
What are you doing here?
01 WILL HAVE TO BE RECALLED ANYWAY.

MODEL 02 IS PROBABLY GETTING HARD RESULTS AT RIIKO IZAWA'S HOUSE EVEN AS WE SPEAK.
MODEL 02!?
THE NEW LOVER FIGURE!? I THOUGHT IT WAS STILL IN DEVELOP-MENT!!
I HOPE IT'S OKAY THAT I INVITED MYSELF OVER...
WE NEED TO TALK.
RIIKO, I'M IN LOVE WITH YOU.

I'LL TALK TO YOUR BOYFRIEND FOR YOU.

WILL YOU PLEASE GIVE ME A CHANCE?

NIGHT AND I HAVE ALREADY ...

WHO'D WANT A GIRL-FRIEND LIKE ME?

HONK HONK

MAYBE JUST ANY-BODY'S ATTENTION WILL DO FOR ME.

IF MODEL 02-- TOSHIKI-- CAN SEDUCE RIIKO IZAWA, HE PASSES THE TEST.
WHICHEVER MODEL WINS RIIKO OVER WILL BE THE PRODUCT LINE WE KEEP. THE OTHER ONE WILL GET SCRAPPED.
RIIKO!
I'LL ALWAYS BE YOUR BOY-FRIEND!!

Absolute
Boyfriend

Act 22: The New Model

RIIKO...
I'M YOUR BOY-FRIEND NOW.
FORGET ABOUT NIGHT.
SHIRA-TORI...
IT'S "SHIRA-SAKI."

I...
I'LL MAKE YOU...
... FORGET ALL ABOUT HIM.
RIIKO!!
OH!
TOTTER
ALWAYS GALLANT
RIIKO!
What a nice young man...

SKWEEK
!!
BA-BUMP
BA-BUMP
BA-BUMP
BA-BUMP
THIS IS GOING WAY TOO FAST!
Hey...
UM...
BA-BUMP
BA-BUMP
!!
!!
BA-BUMP

ZW
IK

ESPECIALLY AFTER STIR-FRIED LIVER WITH GARLIC CHIVES AND SIDES OF ROASTED GARLIC AND KIMCHEE.
It was a dinner of left-overs.
BWUFF
Hey...
Um...
MEANWHILE, NEXT DOOR...

AHHH
THE FRESH NIGHT AIR IS SO INVIGORAT-ING.

I USED TO SHARE LEFT-OVERS WITH RIIKO...
HUH?
What's that hopping over the rooftops?
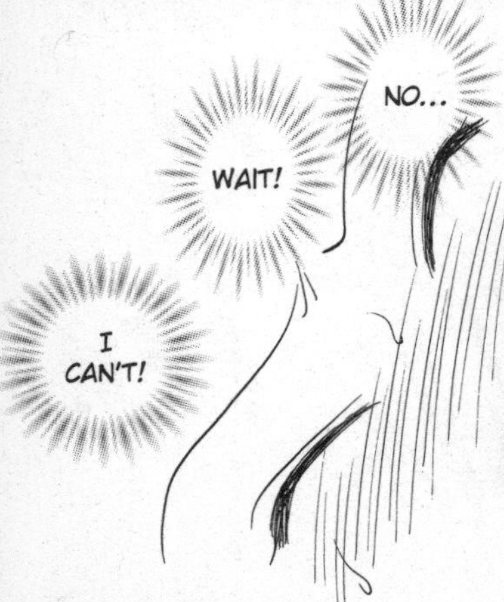
NO...
WAIT!
I CAN'T!

TMP
TMP
NIGHT!!
TMP
TMP

WHOOM
RIIKO!!
GASP
...
YOU ...!!
KRASH

TMP
WHAT WERE YOU DOING TO RIIKO!?
NIGHT !!
WAIT, DID YOU JUST CATCH HIM...!?
WHUP
AND WE WERE JUST GETTING TO THE GOOD PART.

Uh-oh, I'm getting hungry!!
Did I need to say that?
Speaking of which, I went to the recording session of the Absolute Boyfriend drama CD.
How is that related?
It was a marathon session!! All the voice actors are popular. (I'm not worthy.) Well, there's no point in saying much about it yet... Hee hee. But please give it a try. It's hilarious. The bonus track, "Gaku Namikiri's Shopping Network" was so funny, there were tears in my eyes when I heard it. Yes, I know, "Isn't there any romance?" you ask. Well, it's very amusing. You'll see. It also comes with a Kronos Heaven business card, just like the one in the manga. The website listed on it is actually an American site, and its cyber-techno background music is pretty cool.
Americans always have great websites.
Maybe you can pretend you're shopping for a figure. Go check it out!
Meanwhile, I'm still not connected to the Internet (as of June 18)! Surely by the time this graphic novel comes out I will be...

I should go get dinner...

HEH
RIIKO'S BREASTS ARE NICE AND SOFT.
Though small.
DOOM
AAGH!!
I HAVEN'T EVEN GOT TO TOUCH THEM YET!!
WHO
OM

Don't cry about it.

HUH!?
HOW COULD HE BLOCK NIGHT'S KICK LIKE THAT!?

KRAK
WHAP
ISN'T THAT STRANGE?
THUD
UNH...
I'M A BETTER ACTOR THAN YOU ARE.
KRIK KRIK
FINE, LET'S HAVE A SHOWDOWN AND SEE WHICH MODEL IS BETTER.
WHAT!?
LET'S SEE WHICH ONE OF US DESERVES TO BE...

...RIIKO'S BOYFRIEND--
RIIKO'S MINE!!
WOULD YOU LET ME FINISH !?
"MODEL"!?
HE'S KIDDING, RIGHT?

...
Hey...
THAT WAS ...

WAS THAT NIGHT !?
HE WAS LEAPING FROM BALCONY TO BALCONY. NO WAY... THAT'S IMPOSSIBLE.
WIP WIP

HEH HEH
THE KIMCHEE MUST BE GETTING TO ME...
Korean kimchee is the real deal. Watase once got gastritis from kimchee stew.
THOOOM
WHAM
SOSHI, SOME-THING'S GOING ON IN RIIKO'S APART-MENT!

Oh...
PLEASE STOP...
IT'S LIKE THE MATRIX IN HERE!!
I haven't seen Revolutions yet!!
I CAN'T EVEN SEE THEM!!
KRASH
AH!
MAYBE I CAN AT LEAST GET NIGHT TO STOP.
IS THERE ANYTHING ABOUT THIS IN THE MANUAL !?

Umm...
"HOW TO USE THE DOLBY VIRTUAL SURROUND SYSTEM"?
THWAP
WHO NEEDS THAT !?
Is this it?
"IF YOU THINK YOUR UNIT MIGHT BE BROKEN...
"...CALM DOWN AND TAKE A DEEP BREATH."
THWAP
GIMME A BREAK !!

THUMP
DING DONG
DING DONG

RIIKO !?
BAM BAM BAM
WHAT'S GOING ON IN THERE!?

TUG TUG
IT'S NO USE. I'LL HAVE TO TRY ANOTHER WAY...

SOSHI?
DON'T YOU BLACKMAIL ME WITH THIS, MASAKI!!
WHY WOULD I?
I ALWAYS THOUGHT THERE WAS SOMETHING DIFFERENT ABOUT NIGHT.
MAYBE I CAN FINALLY GET TO THE BOTTOM OF IT!

SHOOM
MASAKI, CALL AN AMBULANCE!! SOMEONE JUST FELL OFF--
YOU...
HUH?

...LITTLE JERK !!

STOP IT, BOTH OF YOU!!
RIIKO ...
WAS THAT THE GUY I SAW RIIKO TALKING TO!?
WHAT THE HECK IS GOING ON!?
How did he survive that fall!?

WHAP
STOP FIGHTING! SOMEBODY MAKE THEM STOP!
NO NO NO NO NO
PLEASE STOP FIGHTING OVER ME!
This is crazy!
GRR
YOU'RE... A FIGURE TOO!!
WHAT ARE YOU DOING HERE!?
SHAKE
SHAKE
SHAKE
SHAKE
Figures can bleed.
I'M RIIKO'S NEW BOY-FRIEND.

IT'S YOUR OWN FAULT. YOU WERE WAY TOO SLOW.
YOU'RE SUPPOSED TO BE THE NIGHTLY LOVER SERIES AND YOU STILL HAVEN'T HAD SEX WITH HER.
YOU HAVEN'T COLLECTED MUCH DATA ON THE FEMALE MIND, EITHER.
YOU'RE WORTH-LESS !!
THAT'S WHY THEY MADE ME. I'M THE 02 MODEL.
ALL I HAD TO DO WAS GET RIIKO TO HAVE SEX WITH ME AND I'D HAVE PASSED THE TEST!
BUT YOU HAD TO SHOW UP AND BLOW IT FOR ME!

I DON'T WANT TO GET SCRAPPED!
YOU'RE THE LEMON! IT SHOULD BE YOU!!
GU
UNH...
RK
SCRAPPED !?
NO...
STOP !!
WHAT ARE YOU DOING TO MY BOY-FRIEND !?

SWAK
LET GO!!
TUNK
OW!
RI...
WHY, YOU ...
GRR
YOU HURT MY RIIKO !!
KRAK

HUH?

WAAAH!!

WHY IS NIGHT SO SHOCKED?

HUH?
SKREEK
WHUMP
!?

MODEL 02 TOSHIKI, JUST LOOK AT THIS MESS!
!!
KLAK
Stop, I'm not into men!
What a mess.
GAKU !!
WE BUILT YOU TO BE BETTER THAN NIGHT.
SORRY! I JUST GOT THE WHOLE STORY FROM MY BOSS MYSELF!
NICE TO SEE YOU AGAIN, MISS IZAWA.
YOU'RE TOSHIKI'S LITTLE BROTHER, THE ONE WE MET AT DAIBA!
Toshiki!
I'M YUKI SHIRASAKI, SALES MANAGER OF KRONOS HEAVEN.
I'M GAKU'S BOSS.

WHAT KIND OF COMPANY IS THIS?
TOSHIKI IS OUR LATEST FIGURE UNDER DEVELOPMENT.
THIS WAS ALL A TEST TO SEE WHETHER HE'S SELLABLE OR NOT.
I WAS YOUR GUINEA PIG AGAIN!?
DON'T BLAME ME. I DIDN'T KNOW!
DO THEY NOT TRUST YOU OR SOME-THING!?
SWUMP
OH!
SO THAT NIGHT AT THE HOTEL ...
Oh.
DON'T WORRY. I DIDN'T LET TOSHIKI DO ANY-THING TO YOU.
AND I WAS THE ONE WHO MADE NIGHT GO TO SLEEP TOO.
576667♥ 432836♪ 8#75337.
WHAT THE HECK !?
It was him.

WE'LL BE TAKING TOSHIKI BACK.

WE MADE HIM TOO AGGRESSIVE. WE'LL HAVE TO FIX THAT.

TMP

THIS IS SO UNREAL.

I THOUGHT HE WAS HUMAN ...

GROSS!! TAKE THIS WITH YOU!!

HMPH! LIKE YOU CAN TALK!

MISS IZAWA, THE COMPANY WILL PAY FOR THE REPAIRS.

AND WE'LL GIVE YOU A DISCOUNT ON MAINTENANCE FEES.

BUT WE'RE STILL EXPECTING MORE DATA ON THE FEMALE MIND!
YOU AND 01 ARE VERY INTRIGUING.
Oh.
THE DEAL'S STILL THE SAME. YOU'LL HAVE TO PAY UP IF ANYONE FINDS OUT THAT NIGHT IS A FIGURE!
Don't forget!
C'MON, NAMIKIRI!
We've got to report this to the company.
Wait for me, boss!
GAKU, YOU'RE IN THE WRONG LINE OF WORK.

WHAT'LL HAPPEN TO TOSHIKI?
"SCRAPPED..."
IF I'D HAD SEX WITH TOSHIKI ...
SHIKE
NIGHT !!

THANK GOODNESS.
RIIKO...
I'M SO GLAD...
...I MADE IT IN TIME.

I'M SO GLAD.
ME TOO.
SWUFF
NIGHT...
I'M SORRY.
HE DOESN'T EVEN SEEM TO CARE THAT HE ALMOST GOT SCRAPPED.
BUT...

NIGHT'S NOT REALLY HUMAN.
I'D ALMOST FOR-GOTTEN.
SHOCK
ALL OVER AGAIN

AND ONCE MORE
SHOCK
NO WAY ...
THIS CAN'T BE REAL !!

Act 23: Maintenance

TWEET
TWEET
I...
I DIDN'T SLEEP A WINK!!

MODEL 02, LOVER FIGURE TOSHIKI ...

I WAS THIS CLOSE TO MAKING HIM MY BOY-FRIEND!

I'M GLAD NIGHT STOPPED US IN TIME, BUT...

...IT MADE ME REALIZE THAT NIGHT ISN'T HUMAN.

I KNEW THAT WHEN I BOUGHT HIM...

...BUT SEEING THAT ARM GET BROKEN OFF WAS A REAL EYE-OPENER!!
...Even if it was Toshiki's arm.
CAN HIS HEAD POP OFF TOO?

THAT WAS A SUPER-HUMAN FIGHT AND NIGHT WASN'T EVEN FAZED.
I GUESS IT BROUGHT ME BACK TO REALITY.

CHAK
NIGHT?

早啊!!
理以子♡
(Good morning, Riiko!)
今天
真可爱!!
(You look pretty today!!)
HUH ?
是个好天气呀！
(Nice weather!)
开始吃饭了！
请坐！
(Let's eat! Sit!)
N-N-NIGHT !?
WHY ARE YOU SPEAKING IN CHINESE?
WHAP
WHIRR

?
Como siempre.
(I'm talking like I always do.)
C'MON!! TALK NORMALLY !!
¡Come!
(Eat!)

*
¿Qué has dicho?
(What did you say?)
*SPANISH
HUH !?

THIS FOOD IS TERRIBLE !!
?
SOME-THING ...

¡Vamos a la escuela juntos!
(Let's go to school together!)
...IS SERIOUSLY WRONG WITH NIGHT !!
UH-OH!! THE FIGHT MUST'VE DAMAGED SOME-THING!
DID HE GET HIT IN THE HEAD !?
NIGHT! MAYBE YOU SHOULD STAY HOME TODAY!
CHAK

HEY.

SOSHI!?

NIGHT'S HERE ALREADY?
Pues...
(But...)
Y-YEAH. HE CAME TO WALK ME TO SCHOOL!!

HMPH.
PHEW...
BONK

Didn't sleep all night either.
SHUT UP! IT'S LACK OF SLEEP!
I didn't say any-thing.
A LOVER FIGURE ...
...FROM KRONOS HEAVEN.
?
HE SAW EVERYTHING LAST NIGHT.

I WANTED TO HEAR IT FROM RIIKO'S OWN MOUTH, BUT...
...I'LL WATCH NIGHT TODAY AND THEN DECIDE WHAT TO DO.
HOW CAN HE NOT BE HUMAN?

THEN AGAIN, IT'S POS-SIBLE!
Gackt and Ayumi Hamasaki seem too perfect to be real too!!

I knew that readers were split between Night fans and Soshi fans, but I've discovered that my friends are split as well. (smile) I'd like to know which one is more popular, number-wise. Won't it be sad if one of them gets rejected in the end? Riiko's so cruel. She was unpopular for 16 years, and now she has guys lining up for the first time in her life. I hear that phases like this really happen a couple of times in a person's life. Really!?

Well, manga is my lover. (smile) No, seriously... And it's not exactly a good thing. Oh well, I can't help it. Someone once told me I was made for the manga industry.

Oh, did you know that in America (and in other countries) people get the wrong idea if they see two women holding hands in public? At a convention a couple of years ago, I wasn't feeling well, so I was leaning against my friend as I walked. But that same year there happened to be a rumor going around that I'd brought my lover, so everyone thought we were lesbians. Lesbians!? "We like men!" We screamed into the American skies. It was a joke, right!?

I wish I could have come up with a comeback like, "Next time, I hope to come with my husband! ♥" I'm sorry... (Who am I apologizing to?) I'm so busy with manga right now. It's so sad. But a relationship could get in the way if I were having too much fun working... Oh, I don't think there's anything wrong with being a lesbian, by the way. I hear they can get married in America now.

NIGHT!
TRY NOT TO TALK TODAY, OKAY? PLEASE!
HIGH SCHOOL
IF ANYONE FINDS OUT THAT HE'S A FIGURE...
A MILLION IN CASH!
WAP
HEY THERE.
EEEEK

TOSHIKI
!?

WH-WHAT THE--
I THOUGHT YOU GOT JUNKED!!
THEY UPGRADED ME INSTEAD.
HUH?
HUH?

THEY FOUND A BUYER FOR ME THROUGH THE WEBSITE WHEN WE GOT BACK TO THE OFFICE.
NEWLY UPGRADED

SHE'S A RICH WIDOW! SHE JUST DROPPED ME OFF IN HER MERCEDES!
MY LIFE IS DEVOTED TO GIVING HER LOVE!
I'll give her a massage when I get home. After that? That's between us!
WHAT KIND OF PERSON-ALITY UPGRADE DID HE GET?

SO LET'S BE FRIENDS! ♥
♬
HE'S QUICK TO FOR-GIVE AND FORGET!

...

YACK
Der Wunsch nach einem kleinen,
YACK
kuscheligen Haustier und ein Handy als
ständigem Begleiter sind die wichtigsten···
YACK

AND THEN...

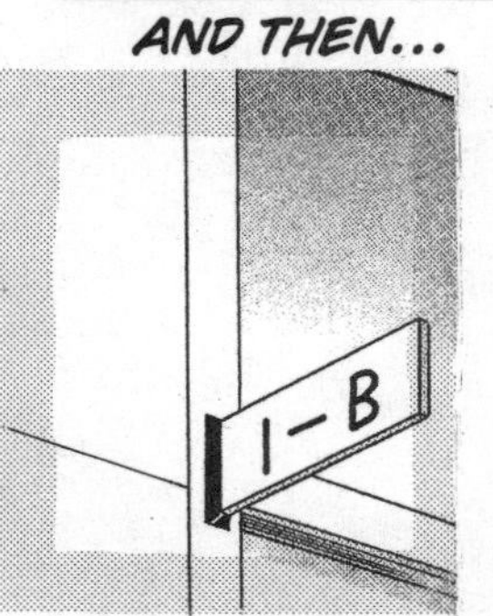
1-B

…Dummerweise läuft das Tier plötzlich
davon und unter bricht…
MR. TENJO!!
THIS IS ENGLISH CLASS, BUT…
…THAT WAS EXCELLENT GERMAN !!
UH-OH, HE'S STILL ACTING WEIRD.
ISN'T HE AMAZING !?
HE MUST'VE LIVED ABROAD!
ISN'T THIS GLARINGLY BIZARRE !?
IS IT A MALFUNCTION OR SOMETHING?
HUH?

NIGHT...
IS THAT SMOKE COMING OUT OF YOUR EAR?
TU NK

HEY...
I SMELL SMOKE!
GULP

IT'S A MAGIC TRICK!!
Ear smoking!!
OH!
THAT'S AMAZING !!
THAT'S EVEN MORE BIZARRE !!

KARATE CHOP
HUFF
NIGHT, WAIT!

WHOA... YOUR HAND'S TURNED THE WRONG WAY.
SHUNK
SHEESH
THAT'S AMAZ-ING!!
ARE YOU PEOPLE BLIND!?
UH-OH!!
WE'VE FOOLED THE OTHERS, SOME-HOW.
Take it out.
BUT SOSHI IS SUSPICI-OUS!!
Well, duh.

N...
NIGHT, COME ON! WE HAVE P.E. NOW!!
TUG
KLANK
SWOOM
FWUMP
WHAT?
NIGHT !?

Nurse's Office
YEAH!
NIGHT HAS BEEN ACTING WEIRD!!
Hmm...
WELL, THAT WAS QUITE A BATTLE.
I WAS AFRAID OF SOMETHING LIKE THIS.
WE'D BETTER RUN A SYSTEM MAINTENANCE CHECK ON HIM!
OH!
TAKE HIM RIGHT HOME! WE'LL MEET YOU THERE!
WHAT!?
WELL, WE CAN'T PICK HIM UP AT SCHOOL! SEE YA!
klik
NIGHT, CAN YOU GET HOME BY YOURSELF?
GEEZ.

SURE!
BOING
Oh!
I CAN UNDER-STAND HIM AGAIN!
Is he fixed !?
AY CAN GOO HOME BY MA'SELF. DINNAE YE WORRY!!
WHO TALKS LIKE THAT?
KRUNCH
I'D BETTER WALK YOU HOME AFTER ALL!!
What?
RIIKO LEFT EARLY?
YEAH!
NIGHT WASN'T FEELING WELL, SO SHE TOOK HIM HOME.
...

WOBBLE
HERE, NIGHT! LEAN ON ME!
Geez.
I CAN'T UNDER-STAND YOU. IS THAT FRENCH?
HE REALLY IS BROKEN.
MAINTEN-ANCE CHECK ...?
WHUD
SWAK
NIGHT !!
THAT MAKES IT SOUND LIKE HE'S JUST A MACHINE.
BUT HE'S SO SOFT AND WARM... HE'S EVEN BREATH-ING...

THUD
A MAINTENANCE CHECK MAKES IT SOUND LIKE HE'S A ROBOT.
I'LL LET GAKU KNOW WE'RE HOME!
HE'LL BE RIGHT OVER!
THEY'LL FIX YOU UP AND...
...YOU'LL FEEL BETTER IN NO TIME!
I MEAN ...
...IT'S NOTHING SERIOUS, IS IT?

NE T'INQUIETE PAS.
(Don't worry.)
FRENCH AGAIN.
JE T'AIME...
(I love you.)

SO WHAT?
SO WHAT IF HE'S A FIGURE?

NIGHT IS NIGHT.
A KISS FOR YOU.
...
GASP
NIGHT ...
HEY ...
NIGHT ...
SHAKE SHAKE
NIGHT !?

NIGHT, WAKE UP!! NIGHT!!
OH NO! NOW HE'S STOPPED MOVING!!

DING-DONG DING-DONG
OH!

GAKU!!
HELLO... WHOA!

Hmm... IT DOESN'T LOOK GOOD.

WHAT!?

HE MUST'VE GOTTEN BANGED UP PRETTY BADLY IN THE FIGHT.

THIS MAY TAKE SOME TIME.
I'D BETTER TAKE HIM BACK TO THE OFFICE AND HAVE HIM CHECKED OUT PROPERLY.
!!
HOW LONG WILL IT TAKE!?
THAT DEPENDS ON WHAT'S WRONG WITH HIM.
HELLO?
IT WAS THAT SERIOUS!?
BUT... YOU CAN FIX HIM, RIGHT?
RIGHT!?
...
OF COURSE.

GOOD THING HE WAS STILL UNDER WARRANTY.
THIS WOULD'VE COST YOU A KIDNEY.
Fiend.
I'LL GIVE YOU A STATUS REPORT LATER!
CHUNK
WHOSE CAR IS THAT?
Kronos Heaven
Kronos Heaven
!!
NIGHT...
HE WAS ONLY PRETEND-ING TO BE OKAY.
I DON'T CARE IF HE IS A FIGURE OR A ROBOT...

I CAN'T GO ON WITH-OUT HIM.
NIGHT IS MY...
DING-DONG DING-DONG
!!
CAN I...
...COME IN?
SOSHI...
SURE.

YOU WALKED NIGHT HOME?
GULP
Y- YES.
THE LIVING ROOM'S KIND OF MESSY. LET'S TALK IN MY ROOM.
WHAT'S SOSHI UP TO?
IT'S A GOOD THING NIGHT'S NOT HERE RIGHT NOW.
...
I HEARD LOUD NOISES LAST NIGHT.
WHAT WERE YOU DOING?
URK
I... I WAS PRACTICING SOME WRESTLING MOVES!!
YOU KNOW, FOR SELF-DEFENSE!

UH-HUH.

I MADE YOU SOME ICED COFFEE!!

IT'S MY SPECIAL BLEND--WITH COCOA! A LITTLE BITTER-SWEET, LIKE LIFE...

!!
NIGHT'S MANUAL !!
I LEFT IT OUT!
NIGHTLY... SERIES?
A KRONOS HEAVEN PRODUCT ...
A LOVER FIGURE ...
...SOLD AT THE LOVER SHOP?
WHAT IS THIS?

OH NO...
I KNEW SOMETHING WAS FISHY. NIGHT'S JUST TOO STRANGE.
KLINK
KLINK
KLINK
I COULD TELL YOU WERE HIDING SOMETHING. AND THAT GAKU IS DEFINITELY A SHADY CHARACTER.
IS NIGHT A ROBOT!?
WHAT THE HECK'S GOING ON HERE!?

HE KNOWS!
I SAW THAT FIGHT LAST NIGHT.
I HEARD EVERY-THING, BUT I COULDN'T BELIEVE IT.
KLANK
SOSHI!
LISTEN TO ME! IT'S NOT...

WHUMP
I LOST YOU...
...TO SOME KIND OF LOVE DOLL!?
SOSHI !?

Absolute
Boyfriend

Act 24:
Open Your Eyes

HUH !?
I CAN'T BELIEVE IT!
SO NIGHT IS A ROBOT?
A LOUSY MANNE-QUIN...
...STOLE YOU FROM ME?
WHAT SHOULD I DO!?

SOSHI, C-CALM DOWN!!
IF PEOPLE WOULD ONLY STOP AND THINK, WARS COULD BE AVERTED!!
YOU'RE THE ONE WHO SHOULD STOP AND THINK!!! ARE YOU CRAZY!?
YOU BOUGHT YOURSELF A MALE LOVE DOLL!
I'M SORRY!!
TWITCH
CALM DOWN?
BUT... WHY?

HUH?
BA-BUMP
I'VE ALWAYS BEEN HERE FOR YOU.

WHY DID YOU HAVE TO DO IT?
WASN'T I GOOD ENOUGH?
BUT ...!
SOSHI ...
... DON'T CRY ...
I CAN'T HELP IT!! IT'S PATHETIC!!
EEK!!
DON'T YOU SEE!?
NIGHT IS JUST A FIGURE!!
DON'T YOU UNDER-STAND WHAT THAT MEANS!?

OF COURSE I DO!

NO, YOU DON'T!!

YES, I DO!

WHAT'S IT TO YOU ANY-WAY!?

SNAP

YOU NEVER TREATED ME LIKE A GIRL!!

KICK KICK

DON'T YOU DARE COMPLAIN NOW!

YOU WOULD'VE... WHAT?
WHAT DID I JUST SAY?
WHY ARE YOU ASKING ME!?
You said it!
WELL ...
WHAT AM I SAYING?
YOU NEVER MADE IT CLEAR!
I LOVE YOU.

I'VE LOVED YOU...
...FOR A LONG TIME.
AND I STILL DO.
I'VE ALWAYS LOVED YOU.

TIMING IS EVERY-THING!!
MAYBE I'M A FOOL, BUT YOU'RE A BIGGER FOOL!!
WH
TO
LATE !!
A
M
OKAY, I SHOULD'VE REALIZED HOW I FELT SOONER, BUT...
Ow!
...WASN'T IT OBVIOUS !?
WHOMP
WHOMP
SHUT UP! SHUT UP!!
YOU DIDN'T HAVE TO BUY YOUR-SELF A BOY-FRIEND!!

MAYBE IT WAS A STUPID THING TO DO...

...BUT NIGHT STOOD BY ME WHEN I WAS AT MY LOWEST!!

HE MAY BE A FIGURE, BUT HE'S WARM AND SUPPOR-TIVE!!

BIP
RIIKO?
GAKU!?
Your timing is incredible, as always.
WE'RE STARTING NIGHT'S MAINTE-NANCE CHECK.
IT LOOKS LIKE IT MIGHT TAKE A WHILE.
NIGHT!
OH NO...
HOW MANY DAYS WILL IT TAKE!?
CAN'T SAY YET. I'LL CALL YOU LATER!
bip
HEY, WAIT!
IS GAKU THAT SHADY SALES-MAN?

SO WHERE IS NIGHT? HE LIVES HERE, DOESN'T HE?
I can't believe I didn't notice. I live next door.
GULP
WELL, ACTUALLY ...

WELL, THAT WAS AN INCREDIBLE FIGHT.
HE WON'T BE BACK FOR A WHILE.

HE BROKE !?

TMP
I'LL BE TAKING OVER YOUR KITCHEN.
WHAT !?

ARE'NT YOU HUNGRY?
GURGH~
OH.

YOU DON'T HAVE TO DO THIS!

NIGHT WAS DOING THE COOKING FOR YOU, RIGHT?

URK!!

THAT'S RIGHT. AND NOW HE WON'T BE BACK FOR A WHILE.

SIGH

S S S S
Hey.
MASAKI, ARE YOU STILL OUT?

I'M NEXT DOOR WITH RIIKO!

YEAH, SO EAT OUT TONIGHT.

OH, I GET IT. GOOD LUCK!

...

BIP

I WANT TO HEAR ALL ABOUT IT.

Is everyone on summer vacation now? There may or may not be an autograph session in late August. (So which is it!?) Maybe I'll wear a yukata!! It's the only chance I'll have to wear one!! Well, I might not if it's too hot. Or will I?
Make up your mind!
Anyway, I wish winter would come soon. I hate the heat, and I don't get a summer vacation anyway. (I'm so ungrateful. ↓↓) I want to go to somewhere like Norway and see the northern lights.
Canada would be good too.
I hear it can change your whole outlook on life!! And I want to see Venice...before it sinks. One day I will, I swear it!
When?
But first I want to go to a secluded hot springs. Will I make it before volume 5 comes out!? Will I be able to finish my work by then!? Oh yeah...issue 2 of *Fushigi Yugi* magazine will be out in August. I've got to work hard! ↓↓
See you in volume 5!

I bought a box of cereal in the U.S.

It was huge.

It was a twin pack, and it was so full that the box was bulging.

This cost less than $3. I ate it every day and didn't run out. In Japan the box would only be half full, and it would be gone in three sittings. What the heck?

OKAY.
"YOU DON'T LIKE GREEN PEPPERS!?"
"OKAY, I WON'T MAKE THEM ANYMORE!"
NIGHT WAS SO EASY TO DEAL WITH.

BUT SOSHI IS AMAZING.
HE CAN COOK, HE GETS GOOD GRADES, AND HE'S HANDSOME.
AND ABOVE ALL, HE KNOWS ME REALLY WELL.

"I LOVE YOU."
BUT IT'S JUST TOO LATE!
Does the dishes though.
WHAT'S THAT SAYING? WE COULDN'T SEE THE FOREST THROUGH YOUR KNEES?
Couldn't see the forest for the trees.

I WAS ABOUT TO BLURT SOMETHING OUT BEFORE, BUT...
WHAT WOULD I HAVE DONE IF I'D KNOWN HOW SOSHI FELT?

UM, IT'S GETTING LATE ...
SOSHI, DON'T YOU NEED TO GO HOME?
WON'T MASAKI WORRY ABOUT YOU?
I'M MOVING IN WITH YOU.
DOOOM
WHAT!?
What are you talking about !?
YOU WERE LIVING WITH NIGHT, WEREN'T YOU?
WELL, YEAH, BUT ...!
AND HE WON'T BE BACK FOR A WHILE.

I MAY NOT BE ABLE TO TAKE HIS PLACE, BUT...
BUT SOSHI--
IT'S TIME FOR YOU TO FACE THE TRUTH.
NIGHT ISN'T HUMAN.
SOONER OR LATER, YOU'LL HAVE TO SPLIT UP.
BUT NIGHT IS...
"I'LL ALWAYS BE YOUR BOY-FRIEND."
WILL HE AGE LIKE WE DO?

!!
YOU NEED SOMEONE LIKE ME.
IT WOULD BE TERRIBLE FOR YOU.
I CAN GROW OLD WITH YOU. ONE OF US MAY OUTLIVE THE OTHER, BUT...
WHAT I CAN DO...
...IS LIVE MY LIFE WITH YOU.
I MAY NOT...
...BE AS AMAZING AS NIGHT, BUT I'LL TRY TO BE.

I'LL NEVER LET YOU FEEL LONELY.
OPEN YOUR EYES AND LOOK AT ME.
WAS I...
...LONELY?
WAS THAT ALL IT WAS?
BUT...

WHAT ARE YOU...
WHAK
...DOING TO MY RIIKO !?
THAT VOICE ...
TOMP
OW!
NIGHT !?
NIGHT !!

HYAH!
SWUP
Oh...
HE'S TEENY !!

BOING

I'M SORRY, RIIKO! WERE YOU WORRIED!?

WHAT HAPPENED TO YOU!?

You're so cute, but...!

WHAT DO YOU THINK?

AHA!!

THE SHADY SALES-MAN!!

THE NAME'S GAKU NAMIKIRI!!

I WAS SURPRISED WHEN I WOKE UP AT THE OFFICE!

HE KEPT DEMANDING THAT WE TAKE HIM BACK HOME!

I wanted to scrap him just to shut him up.

BUT HIS BODY IS STILL UNDER REPAIR.

WE HAVE A LINE OF MINIATURES, SO I ASKED THE TECHS IF THEY COULD DO SOME-THING.

OH. I SEE ...
I WANTED TO BE WITH YOU EVEN IF I WAS LIKE THIS.

NIGHT...
BUT I DIDN'T EXPECT TO FIND SOSHI HERE!
NOW YOU'RE REALLY A FIGURE, NIGHT. A FIGURINE, THAT IS.
HEY!
uh.
snap
HEY!
HEEEY!!!
?
OH NO! OH NO! OH NO!
WHAT ARE YOU YELLING ABOUT!?
I JUST NOTICED YOU!!

DID YOU JUST CALL NIGHT A FIGURE!?
OF COURSE HE LOOKS LIKE ONE NOW...
OH!
RIIKO, I HOPE YOU HAVEN'T FOR-GOTTEN ...
...IF ANYONE FINDS OUT THAT NIGHT IS A FIGURE...
?
SHOCK
YOU'LL OWE US ONE MILLION !!
Remember?
I TOTALLY FORGOT !!

DOOM

A MILLION WHAT?

ALLOW ME TO EXPLAIN. THAT'S HOW MUCH I COST!

DOWN TO THE PENNY!

I SEE... SO THAT'S HOW IT IS.

RIIKO, YOU WERE SUCKERED BY THESE CROOKS.

I OBJECT, SIR!!

What, you're not a crook?

SOSHI, PLEASE! DON'T TELL ANY-ONE!!
OR I'LL... I'LL...
I'LL BE UTTERLY RUINED!
...

IF I KEEP THIS A SECRET...
...WILL RIIKO STILL HAVE TO PAY?
Well...
IT'S TOP-SECRET MERCHANDISE.
I WON'T TELL ANYONE.
BUT...
...HE'LL HAVE TO GO BACK.
HUH?
WHAT?
WHAT KIND OF SOLUTION IS THAT?
YOU CAN SELL HIM TO SOMEONE ELSE!
ANYWAY, AREN'T THERE LAWS AGAINST SELLING SUCH THINGS TO MINORS!?
BUT, SOSHI, I'M...
AND YOU, NIGHT!

YOU'VE BEEN PUTTING RIIKO IN AN AWKWARD SITUATION ALL THIS TIME! AREN'T YOU ASHAMED!?
HMPH
HOW COULD YOU CALL YOURSELF HER BOY-FRIEND!?
I'D... I'D DO ANYTHING FOR RIIKO!!
...
WHAT ABOUT YOU, RIIKO?
HUH?
DO YOU REALLY WANT TO STAY WITH HIM?
You guys are ignoring me.
I...

Hmph!

FINE.

THEN IT'S SETTLED. I'LL BE STAYING HERE TOO.

WHAT? FOR HOW LONG!?

UNTIL NIGHT GETS REPAIRED...

...ALL THREE OF US WILL LIVE TOGETHER. AND RIIKO WILL HAVE TO DECIDE...

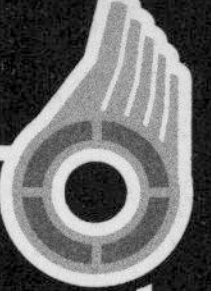

i was listening to one of my MDs (minidiscs) that hold my favorite songs and discovered that the music sounded distorted! it was even worse when i listened to it with headphones. Now i've got to go out and buy the CDs! (i should have already, anyway.) i never knew this could happen to MDs. Cassette tapes can stretch, and dust can scratch vinyl records. Stretched tapes can be fixed by putting them in the fridge, but what can you do to fix MDs?

Yuu Watase

Birthday: March 5 (Pisces)

Blood type: B

Born and raised in Osaka.

Hobbies: listening to music, reading. Likes most music besides *enka* (traditional Japanese ballads) and heavy metal. Lately into health and wellness, like massage, mineral waters and wheat grass juice. But her job is her biggest "hobby"!

Debut title: *Pajama de Ojama* (An intrusion in Pajamas) (*Shojo Comics*, 1989, No. 3)

ABSOLUTE BOYFRIEND

Vol. 4

The Shojo Beat Manga Edition

This manga volume contains material that was originally published in English in *Shojo Beat* magazine, January–June 2007 issues.

STORY AND ART BY
YUU WATASE

English Adaptation/Lance Caselman
Translation/Lillian Olsen
Touch-up Art & Lettering/Freeman Wong
Design/Courtney Utt
Editor/Nancy Thistlethwaite

Editor in Chief, Books/Alvin Lu
Editor in Chief, Magazines/Marc Weidenbaum
VP of Publishing Licensing/Rika Inouye
VP of Sales/Gonzalo Ferreyra
Sr. VP of Marketing/Liza Coppola
Publisher/Hyoe Narita

© 2003 Yuu WATASE/Shogakukan Inc. First published by Shogakukan Inc. in Japan as "Zettai Kareshi." All rights reserved. The stories, characters and incidents mentioned in this publication are entirely fictional.

No portion of this book may be reproduced or transmitted in any form or by any means without written permission from the copyright holders.

Printed in Canada

Published by VIZ Media, LLC
P.O. Box 77010
San Francisco, CA 94107

Shojo Beat Manga Edition
10 9 8 7 6 5 4 3 2 1
First printing, August 2007

www.viz.com

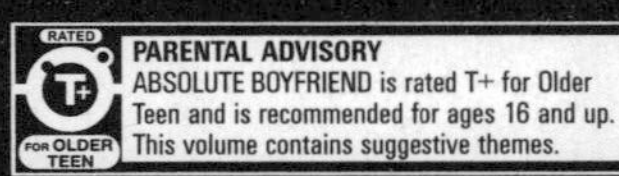

RATED
T+
FOR OLDER TEEN
PARENTAL ADVISORY
ABSOLUTE BOYFRIEND is rated T+ for Older Teen and is recommended for ages 16 and up. This volume contains suggestive themes.

store.viz.com

Tell us what you think about Shojo Beat Manga!

Our survey is now available online. Go to:

shojobeat.com/mangasurvey

WITHDRAWN

Help us make our product offerings better!

3 1901 05403 3867

2001 by Arina Tanemura/SHUEISHA Inc.
04 Yuu WATASE/Shogakukan Inc.
Ouran Koko Host Club © Bisco Hatori 2002/HAKUSENSHA, Inc.

Love. Laugh. Live.

In addition to hundreds of pages of manga each month, ***Shojo Beat*** will bring you the latest in Japanese fashion, music, art, and culture—plus shopping, how-tos, industry updates, interviews, and much more!

DON'T YOU WANT TO HAVE THIS MUCH FUN?

Only **$34.99** for 12 GIANT Issues! **51% OFF** the Cover Price!

NANA by AI YAZAWA

Subscribe Now! Fill out the coupon on the other side

Or go to: www.shojobeat.com

Or call toll-free 800-541-7876

Crimson Hero by MITSUBA TAKANASHI

Backstage Prince by KANOKO SAKURAKOJI

Vampire Knight by MATSURI HINO

Baby & Me by MARIMO RAGAWA

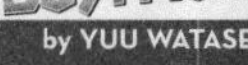

Absolute Boyfriend by YUU WATASE

Absolute Boyfriend © 2003 Yuu WATASE/Shogakukan Inc. Akachan to Boku © Marimo Ragawa 1991/HAKUSENSHA, Inc. CRIMSON HERO © 2002 by Mitsuba Takanashi/SHUEISH
Backstage Prince © 2004 Kanoko SAKURAKOUJI/Shogakukan Inc. NANA © 1999 by Yazawa Manga Seisakusho/SHUEISHA Inc. Vampire Knight © Matsuri Hino 2004/HAKUSENSH

Save OVER 50% OFF the cover price!

Six of the most addictive Shojo Manga from Japan: *Nana, Baby & Me, Absolute Boyfriend* (by superstar creator Yuu Watase!!), and more! Plus the latest on what's happening in Japanese fashion, music, and culture!

Save 51% OFF the cover price PLUS enjoy all the benefits of the SB Sub Club with your paid subscription—your issues delivered first, exclusive access to ShojoBeat.com, and gifts mailed with some issues.

only $34.99 for 12 HUGE issues!

☑ **YES!** Please enter my 1-year subscription (12 GIANT issues) to *Shojo Beat* at the special subscription rate of only $34.99 and sign me up for the SB Sub Club.

NAME

ADDRESS

CITY STATE ZIP

E-MAIL ADDRESS P6BGNC

☐ MY CHECK, PAYABLE TO SHOJO BEAT, IS ENCLOSED

RATED T+ FOR OLDER TEEN

CREDIT CARD: ☐ VISA ☐ MASTERCARD

ACCOUNT # EXP. DATE

SIGNATURE

☐ BILL ME LATER PLEASE

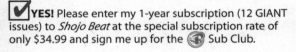

CLIP AND MAIL TO

SHOJO BEAT
Subscriptions Service Dept.
P.O. Box 438
Mount Morris, IL 61054-0438

Canada add $12 US. No foreign orders. Allow 6-8 weeks for delivery.